ALL OF US

All of Us

Stories and Poems Along Route 17

Esther Cohen

Saddle Road Press

All Of Us: Stories and Poems Along Route 17
© Esther Cohen, 2023

Saddle Road Press
Ithaca, New York
saddleroadpress.com

Book design by Don Mitchell
Cover photograph by Matthew Septimus
Author Photograph by Khanyisile Ndaba

ISBN 979-8-9879541-3-3
Library of Congress Control Number 2023940264

Also by Esther Cohen

Book Doctor: A Novel
No Charge for Looking
Unseenamerica
God is a Tree
Breakfast With Alan Ginsberg
Don't Mind Me and Other Jewish Lies
(with Roz Chast)

For Peter

And for every single person in the state of New York

My continuing passion is to part a curtain,
that invisible shadow that falls between people,
the veil of indifference to each other's presence,
each other's wonder, each other's human plight.

—Eudora Welty

Contents

Why

when I try telling strangers
when they ask me
at the library
in the store
who I am
why I live in the country

—I am a person
who meets people often—

I tell them
I don't have a dog
maybe I should
maybe I will
no cat either
I am not a country person
and yet
here I am.

Why Why

When I was small
I'd walk outside
into the back yard.
Like being on the moon.
No picnic table
to sit and eat.
Our house belonged to
a grammar school principal
and her brother.
Rumor was
they were incestuous.
He a high school
history teacher specializing
in Reconstruction.

He'd built a barbecue pit
from stones
he'd found.
By the time we moved in
weeds had filled
the barbecue pit.
We never used it.

MIDDLEFIELD

WE FELL IN LOVE with this peculiar town where we live every summer, *town* too big a word for the sixty people who live here side by side. *Hamlet* sounds British, and upstate New York is as far from British as you can get. There's nothing manicured, nothing too rational. There isn't much of a plan. Three country roads just intersect, and every single one of us has some sort of house on these roads. The houses are not the same, and neither are we.

How we got here is a funny question we often ask one another, at the post office, at the farm stand, at the local supermarket 22 miles away.

What life looks like always depends on where you're standing. Where you stand is what you see.

When I was a very young child, my family had an ordinary dinner table. The table was medium sized, good enough wood but not too good. Probably oak. My mother would cover the table with her mother's white cloth on holidays, but the rest of the time, she'd put down wipe-off placemats. Every single night, my placemat was an apple.

Usually there were only four of us eating. My father, a kind and conventional man who liked order, who liked, for instance, to eat the same meal every single Thursday no matter what (pot roast potatoes and peas, Neapolitan ice cream for dessert, he did not mix flavors), sat in a chair on the left. My mother faced him. My brother and I sat across from one another, always in the very same seats, very same placemats. Apple, Orange, Watermelon, Lemon.

I didn't like looking in the same direction every meal. But the rest of the family did. Maybe half a dozen times over the years I suggested changing seats. No one ever wanted to. They didn't even want to change their placemats.

A while ago, when we were looking to buy a house, when we were lucky enough—because our New York apartment is rent controlled, because we were both working, because real estate in upstate New York was not so expensive—when we decided to buy a house we could live in, our first house ever, maybe even our last house ever, we did not realize how hard it was to have a house, how much always goes wrong no matter what. We didn't realize either that the people you see are part of your view, that the people, all of them, are the real story of Middlefield, our town on County Route 17.

STORIES

MY LIFE IS A COLLECTION of stories. I had an idea when I was very young, maybe eleven, because eleven is a year I remember happening—my teacher was a man named Robert Z, a strong man with many ideas, ideas I'd never heard before—I had the idea then that I still have, that if I were willful enough and lucky, I would be able to find a place where I actually belonged, where people would tell me stories. And I did.

I could ask church lady Paula in the red house down the road—we are all of us within spitting distance of each other on County Route 17—to tell me about herself and she'd explain what it was like when she was young and rode motorcycles with boys and had three sons with a man who left and how she met her current husband because he was stacking peas at her super market and when she grabbed a can his pyramid fell, and he came running.

These stories are our lives. They are what we know and how we say who we are. Our words are breath for us all.

I've been gathering these stories all my life. A lot of them from where I live on County Route 17.

Sometimes people ask why? I make up answers. My grandmother used to say, "Why? Why the Fourth of July?" if someone asked her *why*, and that's as good an answer as any.

Grandma Hannah was my most frequent interview subject. Festooned fabulist born in Romania, she was a strong woman with one long story that lasted a lifetime.

"Every fish has a tale," she liked to say. Her life was a story she never tired of telling. She moved away to California when I was young, but once a year she'd come to visit.

Here's how she moved away. Her one son, my Uncle Max, pulled up to our house in a gold-colored Buick, a car that became a Cadillac in Hannah's later version. Uncle Max was different from other family members. He went to the gym. He wore sharkskin suits. He gambled and had non-Jewish girlfriends instead of the requisite Jewish wife. He made Hannah laugh, and she never once told him what she said to everyone else: go to graduate school. Max had a gravelly voice from whiskey and cigarettes. He did not celebrate Jewish Holidays.

"Pack your bags, Ma!" he yelled upstairs. She and I were playing Library on our porch. I'd make up a book and tell her the plot as an enticement to check it out. They were usually love stories with surprising endings loosely based on what she'd told me. She would play along. "What happened next?" she'd ask, and I would tell her.

We were playing our millionth after school Library game when Max pulled up. He'd driven all the way from California. "It's warm there," he said. "The whole place talks about weather. You'll love it. I found us an apartment on a street near an ice cream store." What she loved most was ice cream. "Let's get out of here, Ma," he said, and by the next morning, Hannah was on the road to another life.

When the phone rings, what I want, what I always want, is a story. A good story. It doesn't matter (really, it doesn't. Not everyone believes me) whether or not it is true. Some people (doctors lawyers engineers health care practitioners scientists in stripes) seem to be so wedded to the truth, to wanting to know EXACTLY. As though there is (really and truly) an exactly.   E v e n my new beautiful yoga teacher, with her perfect name Dolphi and a more or less elegant yogic manner—she is funny, an eye doctor in her day job, she talks and listens, she does not make disparaging remarks about either my hamstrings or my spine—even Dolphi believes in facts. She has a skeleton. The skeleton doesn't lie. How could she not believe that? She teaches yoga. But she's caught up, or so she says, in what is or isn't. I've never heard a good explanation.

My life is a collection of stories. I retell some here for you. There are stories I'm sure I'll remember forever, and then I don't. Others seem to pass right by, but years later, they waft back in.

If I Were a Painter and I Am Not

Today's painting would be wet green
with many birds but the birds
would not be visible. You'd just hear
them. My neighbors who aren't across
the street anymore, they moved to
Florida, they would return and I'd paint
them sitting near their silver barn,
once full of books because they'd
wanted to open a bookstore. I would
paint them back along with Billy and
Anne from the Bronx who left this
road a while ago with their three kids
for Albany so the kids could play
in a playground and not just a big
backyard. And our good friend Stefan
who died a while ago, in my painting
he'd be in his boat riding along
the Hudson River and he'd be smiling.

"DON'T TELL ME you don't understand what I'm saying."
Alexander Bloom was unusually loud. Not quite yelling.
But almost. If he were an ordinary person, someone
who yelled on a regular basis or even raised his voice, it
would have been far less alarming.

But he was a historian, the quiet kind of historian, not
any sort of revisionist radical or revolutionary, not the
rewriting history kind who spoke on Berkeley panels. Or
visited Rachel Maddow. He was considered, soft spoken,
even gentle, the kind of man whose hands were long and
thin, who might have played piano. He didn't, but it was
possible to imagine Alexander Bloom, if you happened
to be sitting next to him at a dinner party, as a piano
player, maybe a violinist.

He wasn't rhythmic, wasn't even musical, but he had
the quiet grace of some academics who've given their
lives to gathering information, who hold onto their
notebooks and figure out a way for those notebooks to
have a logical place somewhere, on a shelf, in a drawer,
in a desk or a cupboard.

His oak file cabinets held soldier-like old fashioned
manila folders, upright, at attention, with titles like Rent
Checks and Water Bills.

"Are you yelling, Alex?" Eli was watching something
in the next room, probably cartoons, but he came into
the living room where we were all sitting, startled by
hearing the unfamiliar sound of Alex's raised voice.

"No," was the reply. And then, seconds later, "Yes."

Eli didn't care about explanations. He didn't seem
to need them. What he wanted, maybe, was just the

reassurance that he heard correctly. That's all. Eli is a listener. He hears and hears.

We all have our roles. Entrenched. But very occasionally, one of us breaks character. "I am dating," he said, and the sound he used for that sentence was far too loud for words. Imagine someone you know very very well, say a sibling or your best friend forever, or Alexander, suddenly shouting the sentence: I Am Dating. It could be followed by a whoopee, YES thank goodness, or it could be Oh No.

Alexander Bloom had dated on occasion. He is, in the words of a friend named Annette, a catch. Catching him, she says, would be a good thing. He is articulate. He has a job. He would be a reasonable companion, on time and kind.

Annette believes life is about expectations. She married a man who is perpetually late. Being late drives her crazy. Alex would not have that problem. Maybe, she says, she should have married Alex. Not that romance ever came up. They have been friends for years. Annette married her husband Larry because he was funny. She doesn't think he's funny anymore.

Alex's dating, like other parts of his life, has been in Moderation. He's a moderate kind of guy. He operates sequentially: one, two, three, four. Leaping is not in his repertoire, and neither is shouting.

He is a person who keeps his everyday soap in a clear plastic soap dish, the top always closed. We have been making fun of this for years.

Some women have pursued him. He is neat and well-read. One woman was especially aggressive. A young Judge in the Boston courts, well-connected, high powered. A woman with an admirable handshake and plans. We met her once at a fund-raiser for Cesar Chavez, a loud crowded good-natured activity.

Alexander Bloom is very thin. Not lithe. Just thin. One long line from head to toe. An easy line, not moving.

The boys draw all of us, and dutifully place those drawings on the refrigerator. All three sides are full with their portraits. They pick colors for each of us, so that we can be sure who they are depicting. Alexander Bloom is navy blue, that Crayola navy that isn't all that dark. His head is always small, balanced, a ball on a stick figure.

Manuel is bright green, a green that seems to come from underwater more than from this earth. Even so, they draw him wearing a T-shirt that says I Love to Mow.

Nick is brown. His face is one big mustache, thick line like a smiley face, handlebars curling up, and he's holding a guitar in his left hand.

My portrait is red, and it's mostly hair, big red corkscrew curls like Orphan Annie, moving crazily out of my head. I never have a body in their drawings.

"What are you talking about, Alex?" Sometimes Manuel could be fearless. "Why is dating such a big deal? Who doesn't date?"

"Well, you don't for one," Alex replied.

"That's hitting below the belt."

"Exactly," he said. "You're not exactly Don Juan."

"I didn't say I was," said Manuel, who had a few intense relationships in his day. One in particular, a woman named Sophie, obsessive acupuncturist who insisted on carrying needles with her wherever she went, seemed to last and last; but then one day Manuel announced how over it was, and no one was surprised.

"Why so adamant?" Manuel continued. "What is it about dating that causes the big shout out, the out of character explosion? What's going on? Maybe you should try to figure that one out, Alex. And when you do we'd like to know. Because this involves all of us. I'm going deaf," he said. "But not that deaf. I assume you're not shouting for me."

Alex is a pale person, somewhere grey and white, an indoor library type who likes the sun, even likes the kind of mild hiking that involves water bottles and gorp. His attractiveness is in his kind, gentle manner. He wouldn't hurt anyone, innocent or not. Even flies are not his enemies.

"You're wrong," he shouted—actually shouted—with an adamance he never exerted. He was an emotional moderate, always well-considered. "What I do is my business," he said to Manuel, one of his best friends in the world. "It isn't yours. In fact it isn't any of yours. The idea that my life is about your life too is really crazy." His natural greyish complexion turned bright red, and he actually started to sweat.

Normally, when something happens that is awkward or difficult, Nick, mild-mannered sensitive Nick, makes a joke. He figures out a way to make everyone laugh. Laughing has saved us all. But Nick, a quick responder, never thrown off guard, is silent, confused.

"I mean it," said Alex, and then he stood up, not quite tall, awkward as ever, and with his usual endearing Alex gesture he nervously smacked his lips, making the funny sound whistling sound of nervous air.

Then he turned to address us all. We were sitting, as always, in our kitchen, a kitchen that promotes sitting as much as it does meals. A dozen people can sit in the kitchen, no problem, large square, not open and empty like loft space. There's nothing even a little Japanese about our kitchen, which is always full of people, of bowls in every color and shape, of enough glasses to comfortably give 100 friends a large cold drink. As for drinks, the choice is wide-ranging, and it would be difficult to come up with a drink request for something we don't have, from Brazilian Cachaca to Diet Coke to absinthe.

The kitchen is not the place where we disagree, where problems happen. That's been more the dining room. That Alexander Bloom broke precedent, suddenly, with unexpected anger and even with a kind of new vehemence, made all of us uneasy.

"I'll say this," he said, addressing his best friends in the world, really, the people he'd shared a life with for years, who knew, or thought they did, every single thing about him, addressing us as though we were an unruly history class, unable to hear his lesson. He was pale when he faced us, and we, a generally noisy group, an oddly happy mixture of friends who believed that we would be friends forever, as naïve as good friends can be, and as well intentioned, we who believed we'd grown up together and would grow old together on our porch, moving back and forth in the rockers we chose so carefully, listening as much as possible to Otis Redding, to old Beatles songs, to James Brown and Pete Seeger, we who had vaguely planned out the future to take place right here, right where we were, couldn't help but be surprised with the brief speech Alex gave.

He was not a spontaneous person, and when we talked about this later, which we did over and over, trying hard to remember all his words, which was not easy, we all agreed on the first few sentences.

He stood up from his favorite chair, painted the dark green he liked so much, 50's green that looked like barbecues and watermelon; there he was, so nervous, speaking to us as though we were not his best friends in the world, people he'd lived with for years, who he talked to every day. He cleared his throat with the dry hacking sound that often precedes unfortunate words, in a nervous voice that some people have, including Alexander Bloom. His voice raised and shaky, so shaky, it was hard not to feel very bad for him. Because, of course, we loved him, loved him the way you love some people forever.

"I'm going to become a different person," is what he said, his first sentence; and I immediately pictured a lifeguard at a swimming pool, god knows why, one of those Olympic swimmer types with a whistle around his neck, sort of happy go lucky, from Costa Rica where he'd learned to surf.

"This doesn't work," he said, and I felt as though all of us were an unfortunate spouse in *As The World Turns*. "I'm off," he said. "In another direction."

Then he walked out of the room, right into his car, his old Ford that had belonged to his brother in Long Island, his brother who changed his car every five years and gave the old one to Alexander Bloom.

We could only wonder where he was going.

How We Found Our Real Estate Lawyer

When we were looking for a real estate lawyer
people gave us names of people they said were
difficult expensive sometimes both. Unpleasant lawyers.
I was wearing a favorite lime green dress
when we stopped at Shoprite to buy food for dinner.
Back of my dress bunched into my body by mistake.
Kind woman walked over while I was choosing leeks
to say she'd walked all around Rome one whole day
with the back of her dress like mine. I asked
after thank you if she knew a real estate lawyer
she said for 37 years she sold real estate
she'd give us the number of the person
she liked most. And we went there and when
I called her after to say thank you
she said, "Don't forget to check behind."

Arlette's Husband

ARLETTE ARRIVED IN THE MIDDLE of a snowy winter day. She came from El Salvador, where she lived in one those villages that seem so idyllic to tourists. She was poor, neat and ambitious, God-fearing and certain that in the United States she could find what she needed. Through a friend, she got a job cleaning houses, big and small homes in neighborhoods all over Albany County and although it took her forever to get to work on county buses—she lived in government housing in a neighborhood that bordered on rough—she didn't mind. She would dress for the day in one of her neat-flowered dresses, well-pressed, and she would apply her make-up as carefully as though she were going to Communion. She looked beautiful on those trips, untouchable, and Christian.

She carried her work clothes in a small brown shopping bag. Most of her clients gave her their keys so she didn't see them while she walked through their homes, mopping, vacuuming, dusting their counters, paying attention to what was theirs, wondering out loud how so many of them could be so slovenly. Why they didn't care for themselves. She loved wax and polish and used whole bottles of both every day. Before she left, she usually wrote a note: *This is from Arlette,* she'd begin, and draw a flower or two. *I'd like more polish that smells like fresh lemons and more wax for your floors.* That's all she ever said, and they would do what she asked because Arlette's houses, when she left them, looked as perfect as she did. She was good at creating order. She striated books and records on their shelves, and lined up shoes so they seemed to be in a perfect unalterable row. While she cleaned, she hummed "Onward Christian Soldier," or "Jesus Gentle as a Lamb," often raising her voice to a boisterous shout.

Despite all this order and calm, Arlette was not yet happy. The men she went out with, although she didn't like to say the word out loud, were married. They took her to movies, to steak dinners with bottles of red wine, to loud cheerful plays, always out of town. If she hadn't been so serious, she might have fallen in love with a particularly handsome married man named Walter. He was from Dominica, which he called the Caribbean diamond, and he would often joke that someday they'd fly back together and build themselves a big white house right on the beach. Of course she'd heard that promise before, but when Walter said it, she wanted to believe. She laughed and flirted and even became pregnant with Walter's child, but she knew he'd never leave his wife. Walter already had three children, and he loved them. On holidays like Thanksgiving, Arlette would prepare a big meal for Walter even though she knew he ate at home. He'd stop by anyway and eat to make her happy.

Arlette got pregnant one Thanksgiving Day, before Walter ran home to his turkey. She waited until New Years Eve to tell him. He was taking his wife to dinner, but first he stopped off at Arlette's with a dozen long-stemmed roses. She gave him a glass of champagne and they toasted to what might happen in the new year. Walter was unemployed, though he kept thinking a job was right around the next corner. A handsome handsome man, Walter knew how to make his women happy. Arlette didn't mind so much about his lack of work because he had some time to see her, but now that there was a child on the way, she thought he should get a job. She knew his wife worked hard, but Arlette did not know the details of where.

"To you," she said.

"To us," said Walter.

"To all of us," answered Arlette.

He instantly turned a funny red. "You can't have it," he said. "I don't have any money. My wife will have a fit."

"I have to," she said. "I've always wanted a child."

"How will we support him?"

"It's a girl," she said. "I can tell. And when the time comes, we'll find a way."

She felt less certain than she actually sounded. Walter stopped calling, and then she began to worry more or less all the time. She worried about what to tell her family in El Salvador. She worried that she'd have to fly home without any of her dreams.

Arlette was a person full of plans. She wanted to go to school, to get a professional job, to work in a hospital maybe, or be a dental hygienist, to buy a house someday with a yard and a fence and a feeder for birds. She wanted a husband who took her for rides on Saturdays and bought her perfume on her birthday. She knew that Walter was already married, but she didn't realize that a child, even his own, would cause him to disappear.

Arlette worked until late July, when she couldn't carry around her weight any longer. In the middle of a Monday night in August, Arlette went to the hospital alone, where she had her baby, a sweet little girl who died. The doctor said it was because of her unformed lungs, but Arlette really believed it was because Walter was married. She cried for the whole month of August, and put his flowers out in the hall when they finally arrived. She sent him a postcard telling him his daughter was dead and mailed it right to his home. She knew his whole family would see it. In September, she went back to work. The first few weeks, she wore her cleaning clothes out in public to walk to work. She felt fat and tired and she was always sad. She had named her daughter Rose, and over and over again she said the words, "Rose is Dead" like a prayer.

After a while, she began to start singing, and then to wear her flowered dresses again. Men talked to her again, and by winter, she was smiling. Christmas Day, she was all alone, and she spent the day opening presents from El Salvador.

At four in the afternoon, she went for a walk to the little grocery store just a block from her house. They were always open. The Haitian man who ran it was her friend. She dressed carefully because it was Christmas, and she even made up her eyes. Arlette suddenly felt better, as though the New Year would bring her closer to the life she imagined. A handsome young man was in the store, scraping off instant lottery tickets. Although it was winter, he wore a bright blue baseball shirt under his jacket and no sweater.

He winked at Arlette, saying, "Can I interest you in a holiday movie?" and then he bowed right in front of her. He really bowed.

"Are you married?" she asked him, looking straight into his eyes. He looked like he was only 20 years old, but that didn't necessarily mean very much.

"Not at all," he said, and didn't look away. "I've been waiting for someone like you."

And then he bowed again, more deeply.

"Not today," she smiled at him. "I have plans for later." Though she knew she liked him.

"Tomorrow then," said the fellow who introduced himself as Albert. He seemed pleased her name was Arlette. "Double A's," he said. "Very lucky."

She gave him her number, and early the next morning he called. At 8:00 a.m. Albert really was single. He'd even finished school and wanted to keep going. Albert studied biology and earned his living working in a lab. But he'd been a flamenco dancer in Guyana, where he was born. Albert was as handsome as Arlette was pretty. Together they looked as though they belonged.

He planned to move to the state of California to continue his studies. His intention was to buy a house somewhere not far from the water, a house with a view. Before that, their wedding day.

Hairport Customers

1

Claudia, 70
"I'd like to shave my head
just to see if I can handle it."

2

Mary, mid 40's:
"My husband has a good job
in the toll booth on the Thruway.
But he only cares about golf.
Watches golf on TV.
Reads golf magazines.
Plays golf on his time off.
I'm thinking of leaving.
I hate golf."

3

Sam, 22:
"I want to be
something like
a man. What I mean is
just not a young girl."

Gay Sarah

Gay Sarah named herself Gay Sarah although there were some people who thought her first name was Gay. But it was Sarah. Gay Sarah—a photographer of some talent although she was not as talented as she'd like, no Helen Levitt or Robert Frank, two people she loved—Gay Sarah taught at Bard College, a beautiful school for rich kids, in one of those perfect-looking towns in upstate New York along the Hudson River. She photographed body parts, not just her own but other people's and she had a whole series called *Where Did My Appendix Go?* Her pictures were witty black and whites, and she'd had some minor success with a few galleries, and now with her new exhibition in Hudson.

Twice a week, she commuted from the East Village. Bard was a Good Job and for that she was grateful. A teacher of hers in graduate school at Parsons went to Bard. And he hired her. She wasn't completely sure why, though maybe he liked her pictures enough, and had an instinct that teaching is what she wanted. She hadn't known that at the time, wouldn't have said even five years ago that she should teach. She was surprised at how much teaching suited her.

When she'd lived in the East Village, she'd lived with Elaine. Sarah took Elaine home with her one night from a party, to her one room apartment on 1st and not too far from Thompkins Square Park, a minute away from Russ and Daughters, a short walk to her favorite neighborhood, the Lower Lower East Side, right below Katz's deli, where her grandparents, both of them, arrived when they came from Poland and Ukraine. She loved it there, and although she knew that her happiness walking through those streets had little to do with the difficult life she knew they lived—factories, crowded apartments, little money—still being on those very same streets made her happy.

Elaine was different. She said she was a Unitarian and Sarah pictured her baking pies one after another: apple, peach, cherry, blueberry—then starting all over again. Seven years they lived together.

After a relationship ends it's not so easy to remember what happened in the beginning, but when Sarah thought about her life with Elaine, their early times together, what she remembered was happiness. They were compatible enough, and though theirs was not like the usual combustion that Sarah knew, fiery mood swings, violent declarations of love and intense dislike and absolute passion, they got along. Sarah taught photography and carried her camera wherever she went. Elaine taught too: graphic design at FIT. They were busy. They had a circle of good friends who lived mostly downtown, and they often gathered together somewhere to celebrate as much as they could. Infinite brunches, infinite dinners. Pizza on the corner with friends. They even went on hikes, although Sarah was not a hiking type, but Elaine, lifetime member of the Audubon Society, knower of male and female birds, Elaine was a hiker and a camper. She even had a regulation backpack with a Swiss Army knife and twine.

Sarah took Elaine to movies and movies. Once a week at least they went to the Film Forum or Anthology Film Archives or somewhere anywhere to see A Good Movie. Their tastes were not the same—Sarah was a movieaholic and could sit through more or less anything, and Elaine, a serious person for a hiker, Elaine tended to like clear messages, a Reason why the movie was made. Their discussions after were often interesting—Sarah trying to persuade Elaine to follow her taste and judgement, Elaine strong in her own opinions, not backing down. One of their biggest fights ever was about Michael Moore. Elaine said, "Yes," and Sarah said, "No." But apart from movies good or bad, they didn't argue much. They were compatible enough. But one day in her shrink session with Barbara, Sarah heard herself explaining in a way that surprised her more than it did Barbara that she wanted more than Elaine.

Barbara was a patient woman. She spent her days listening. She looked across her room, the walls painted light yellow, nothing too strong, and even her photographs on the wall across from her—a black and white landscape, a woman's face—looked muted.

"What do you want from this relationship?" she asked.

And Sarah surprised herself by saying, "I Want Out. It's not a relationship. Not really. I can't remember the last time we had sex, and that doesn't seem to bother Elaine. When I raise the problem, she changes the subject. And besides," she said, "in the end we don't have all that much in common."

Barbara didn't say Yes or No. She just listened for a while.

"I am not unhappy, exactly," Sarah began. Apathy isn't the right word either. I guess I just feel Meh."

She'd never used the word Meh in her life.

But Barbara nodded, as though she heard Meh all the time. "Tell me more," is all she said.

"I'm going to do something completely uncharacteristic tonight," Sarah said. "I'm going to go home and pack my overnight bag and take the train upstate to visit my friend Gwen."

Barbara nodded again and Sarah left for home. Elaine was sitting in the center of the couch. She did not sit left or right. She knew where the exact center was, and that's where she sat when she was alone. When Barbara was home, she moved over a little. Always to the right.

"I'm going to visit Gwen in Kerhonksen," Sarah said. Nothing less and nothing more.

Elaine did not ask why. "OK," she said. Just: OK. "Will you eat first?"

"I'll pack a sandwich," was her reply.

"A sandwich," Elaine repeated but she didn't say one more word. Not even goodbye.

And Sarah walked out the door as though she'd never been inside. She was just going Somewhere Else.

Gwen was an old old friend. "Why not move upstate?" she inquired on the third day, when Sarah said she needed a change, a very big change.

They drove around in Gwen's car looking at small houses, houses that seemed reasonable to buy. She'd wanted to live in an apartment all her life. She'd grown up in a house, a small wooden house in an old factory town in Massachusetts. They made ball bearings there. An apartment was all she wanted ever since she was a child.

But now, driving around with Gwen through small town after small town with Dollar Stores along the way, gas stations, diners that looked the same as the diners she remembered from her childhood, that was the life she suddenly wanted. A house where she could live.

In a week they found a yellow house for $85,000 on a small piece of Catskill Creek, just off Route 17. The woman who owned it was moving to California and she wanted to leave her furniture too: two beds and a couch and a kitchen table with four chairs and a cheap and sufficient round barbecue in a place where it belonged. In the back yard next to the stream.

Sarah surprised herself by going to the bank with Gwen and giving them the $5,000 necessary. A miracle that she had the money. An equal miracle that she could turn it over.

And just like that she moved upstate. For good, whatever *for good* meant.

And one day two years in, while she was at Shoprite buying food for dinner—she cooked simply, but still, she cooked—in the organic vegetable section, while she was looking at beets, she met Renee. They have lived together in their little yellow house now for many years.

OF NEIGHBORS WHO FALL IN LOVE WITH ONE ANOTHER

There's something sexy
in a high school way
about neighbors.
Maybe that's why I've heard
this story 1,000 times.
Martha told it today
when we were all
in the post office.
Famous artist—
with a wife and five sons,
every single son
a drummer,
not even one
bass guitarist—
he fell in love
with his directly-across-the-street
neighbor—
married choreographer
two children of her own.
They ran away—
they are actually both
real marathon runners—
they ran away
to another small town
just three miles away
from here. Will they
both fall in love
with their neighbors again?

MIRANDA, THIS MORNING

Cleaning our house,
she stopped the vacuum cleaner
turned it off
she doesn't usually turn off
the vacuum cleaner
her white noise—
my guess is Miranda
sleeps with her vacuum cleaner nearby
just in case—
this morning she turned it off.
"Hava,"she said. I knew it was important.
"Hava," she repeated
with insistence.
"I hated my fourth husband
and now he's dead.
Last week I visited a clairvoyant.
She saw him floating
up there and heard him shout,
Forgive Me Miranda!
'Never!' I shouted.
He can keep floating
wherever he is
for the rest of
eternity. And you
know what else?"
Miranda added, moving toward
her vacuum cleaner to let me know
her story was nearly over.
"The clairvoyant agreed with me.
'I can see he's a shmuck,'
she said."

WHAT REALLY HAPPENED

While we're here
I try not to think
about ever leaving.
Sitting on this porch
as though I can stay forever
as though I can memorize
how this feels—
sounds of birds
their names I'll never learn,
this porch a treehouse
not so far above the ground,
unfading light yellow
painted by Howard who told me
his brother Robert married
a woman he met in jail.
She was getting her PhD
at the Columbia School
of Social Work said Howard.
She was studying prisons,
studying Robert,
"Irresistible just like me,"
said Howard.
They married in jail.
Howard brought them to the porch
to visit. Robert and Anita PhD,
that's what he called her,
they all sat down and told me their version
of jail and love and Anita PhD's
thesis about Robert.
"I'll stay when they leave," said Howard,
"to tell you what really happened."

MADE IN RUSSIA

OUR NEIGHBOR, Ezra, is a contrary and difficult man who is likable nonetheless. Because he has a sense of humor, and because he likes Chekhov, especially *Lady and the Dog*. The truth is, though, that he's a right-wing nut job, with I Love Trump and Rush bumper stickers still on his truck. Fox News is his God, and when I asked him what he thought his hero Chekhov, the dissolute intellectual, might think of them, what he said was, "Chekhov is dead. Case closed." It's impossible to argue with that.

He's 50 years old, and a Libra, not that Libra matters to him. Though he tells his customers if he thinks they want to know. He makes very beautiful furniture, mostly tables and chairs too expensive to buy. He earns his living doing carpentry exclusively for liberal New Yorkers with weekend homes nearby. Mike is often his assistant. Mike likes Ezra.

Ezra says all liberals want to talk to him about is Donald Trump and Rush Limbaugh. He says they even ask him questions like, "Why did Elton John agree to play at Rush's fourth wedding?" Ezra says it's a little like strangers stopping actors who play doctors on TV and asking about their medical problems.

I am trying to write a young adult novel this summer. It's in verse. I read a little to Eli every night even though he doesn't understand a word. My biggest fear is that he isn't going to be a generational. And that maybe it's Freud. Anyway, I write a line and walk around for an hour and then if I'm lucky I write another line. Sometimes I walk outside to check in with Ezra—we live three doors apart. Everyone else is gone all day.

One day when Ezra was painting our house, he was scraping our house by hand, I asked him what he believes, really. "So, what do you believe?" I asked, offering him one of Mike's cookies. Pistachio test. Hoping if I give something to him, he'll give something to me.

He came down from his ladder to reiterate first that he doesn't like our color choice, light beige. He thinks all houses should be white, no question. He is tall and thin, a true Jeremiah. He could pass for an aesthetic type in his plain grey, nicer than Fruit of the Loom, T-shirt and his loose I-am-a-House-Painter-See-Me-Paint pants. He's one of those men who is eternally boyish. He looked at me and smiled. His smile is what's best. It actually moves across his face in a slow and convincing half-moon manner, and it is possible, seeing him smile, to forget the whole Trump/Rush thing, or maybe just believe it's some kind of peculiar joke.

Ezra looked at me. I am exactly the kind of person he claims to detest. And still his smile could not have been nicer.

"I believe," he said, "in Russian food. That's the very reason I've decided I want a Russian bride. Yes, you heard me. The food is carefully prepared. Unaltered by politics or culture, by any outside factions. My belief is that women are very much like their food. I've thought about this for years," he continued. "I've got six candidates. Women I met online. I found them on a few websites and I write every day to all the candidates."

"Candidates?" I said. "This is too weird. It sounds like your own personal game show." He smiled at me again. Twice in one day.

"You'll be one of the happiest people around here to have a Russian neighbor, I am sure," he said. "Picture the meals."

"I don't want her to cook for me." Even as I said these words, I knew it wasn't entirely true. But still. The idea of a mail-order bride seemed so anachronistic and so wrong. I didn't know what to say.

Ezra kept me informed about his search, about the six women who made his final round. They each had one child. All the women described the meals they'd cook when at last they met.

Ezra's an anti-foodie more or less. He believes foodies are all crazy liberals who don't have much else to think about. He's a practical man who buys cheap coffee, whatever's on sale, and carries it around all day in an old plaid thermos. He'd never have a Duncan Donuts Latte, and he thinks that Starbucks is somehow Socialist because it's expensive and comes out of Seattle. Even so, he claimed that Russian women making him his meals had an incomparable appeal.

The six women became more real over the summer. They all used American names: Betty, Polly, Sally, Sue, Nancy, and Carol. I asked if he was falling in love with their pictures, or with their translator's words.

"Love," he said "is a Hollywood idea. I'm in like with them all."

"Can you be in like with a person from their emails?"

"Now you sound like a suspicious capitalist. So untrusting."

I didn't want to like him better for this process, but I did. He who was so neat, so controlled and controlling, who planted privets in a straight line in front of his house, so Germanic, unalterable, trimmed trimmed trimmed, was making a major life decision. He'd never been anywhere except New England, New Jersey, California, and a few places like Albany. He'd been to

New York City once, just to the top of the Empire State Building, and then right back to his cousin's house on Long Island. He said New York City was a good place for him to find concrete evidence about What was Wrong with Liberals. When he said that sort of thing, although I knew he meant it, I didn't react the usual way. I'm not sure why.

Now, suddenly, for reasons only he knew, he was flying to Russia to make a family. Nancy, he said, was his number one choice. Nancy's daughter was named Joy. Nancy told him her favorite book, oddly enough, was *Anna Karenina*, but that didn't seem to bother Jeremiah. Yet *Anna Karenina* was a novel he disliked. In August he flew to Moscow. He brought pictures home of Nancy and Joy, and there they were, smiling at him, standing in front of famous landmarks. "We got along very well," he said.

But just in case, because you never know, not really, how any story ends, he went to visit Polly and her daughter Susan, ate their meals. "All good," he declared. He met them and visited their landmarks. He brought home a sheaf of pictures for reference.

"You're not buying a pet," I said when he showed me.

"What do you think marriage is? It's just an arrangement," he said. "Look at you and Nick."

I remembered the first time Nick smiled at me, so full of emotion and wit, sad and happy all at once. I knew I could look at his face forever. Would meeting him on the internet have made any difference at all?

The next summer, Ezra went to Russia to teach English for three weeks in August. The job was in the town where Beloved Number One lived (He called her First Bride). Nancy took his English class. She brought him his lunch in a beautiful metal box she'd painted with birds. In September, when he walked over to let me know where things stood, he said, "This is It. They're coming." Next May, when the beauty is absolute here, and when Joy's school is over for the summer. They planned to start their new life as a family. They both wanted to marry: American Husband Russian Bride.

Ezra said Nancy intended to make his favorite pierogis with family recipe pancakes and very fresh plum sauce for their wedding feast.

He's not Mister Social. I don't think I've ever once seen an unfamiliar car in his driveway. Emergency repair people are Ezra's only guests. In one fell swoop he would be transformed: husband, father, family man. Lawn mower, beer in a can, ball games on television. He wanted, or so it seemed, to be one of those men, to live in a way he imagined most men lived: breakfast lunch dinner. Labor Day Halloween Thanksgiving Christmas New Year's. Maybe he'd even have Russian turkey. Life would be a series of carefully orchestrated events, appropriate dinners, birthday celebrations.

I watched his life the way we tend to watch one another, with curiosity, with trepidation, and some amount of hope. I didn't want to like Ezra, didn't want to like a Rush Limbaugh listener even a little, to befriend someone whose very belief system was horrifying. Still, there was a fascination. Maybe anthropological.

Nick did not share this point of view, but that didn't stop me.

Ezra went to Russia, disappeared for a while without bothering to say goodbye. He was oblivious more than rude. He was a man who lived in his own small bubble. But there was another side too, the Chekov side. He had the ability, however infrequent, to make a revealing personal remark, often enough for you to believe that maybe he knew what he was doing. "I'm unevolved," he'd say. "I've got emotional Asperger's." Or, "I'm adamant about my boyishness, although I'm actually fifty."

Ezra left to marry a Russian bride, and while he was away, I could think of absolutely nothing else.

He did not return until the last week in August. Irene at the post office told all of us at the one-room post office picking up our mail, our CVS discount flyers, school board notices, septic cleaning ads, all those vestiges of the lives we still lived in this odd place in the middle of nowhere.

"He arrived," she announced to the six people gathered in the post office, awaiting word. "Bride and child in tow. It was after midnight when their car pulled up and I couldn't see all that much except luggage. Happy or unhappy? It was hard to tell from across the street."

No streetlights in Middlefield.

"If he's right though," Molly said, "at the very least we can all expect a good meal."

Big Old Maple Tree is Gone

Coming home from the post office
Saturday afternoon looked like rain
walking up the driveway I heard
a sound, loud cracking right next to me;
big tree on the front lawn of the house
next door fell, hitting the house
instead of me, coming down
on the porch roof soft dent broken beam
two windows gone,
and then there was the tree
missing from where it stood in the sky.
I had taken that tree for granted,
assumed I would walk by it forever
and the tree would be
right there where it belonged.

For So Many Years I Wanted to Tell You This

My grandmother said that to me all her life. All her one long story life. I miss her stories still.

I am a person who is always starting over. Every day. Trying to tell the very same story.

Last night I confessed to a stranger at the library, a woman I'd never seen before, one of those friendly broad faced strangers who probably has eleven grandchildren— she didn't even tell me her name—last night I confessed to her that beginnings are all I care about. Not all those inevitable endings. Which I know too well.

There's no rule, not a good one anyway, that says a story can't begin in the middle. Some people like endings first. Who Did The Thing, and what led up to the Major Act: Betrayal, Desperation, Injustice, War.

I don't even know where the middle of anything might be. Probably one of those Greeks made a rule about order that we've all been following forever, but 1,2,3 can just as easily be 2,3,1, depending.

We've been in Middlefield for twenty years, twenty years that have been both long and short. I have always measured my life in summers. Some of us—there must be a study somewhere—had these fragrant summers when we were children. By fragrant I don't mean that we went somewhere else. My friend David says, "Most of us summer where we winter."

It's not about where we are. It's more what happens there. How we feel about peaches and heat and water and not having to cover our bodies with anything much, what happens to us when the structure of school, of work, of life is replaced by long open days, days that begin so slowly that it's hard not to wonder if mornings could last forever. Days that end with deep skies. Of course there are skies the rest of the year, but in summer there's a different, better, bluer sky, a sky you want to lie beneath forever.

Our days vary wildly. Sometimes long afternoons like those long afternoons that happened when we were children, where light and possibilities have no limits, where we believed that life is infinite. How long and fragrant and happy were the afternoons. When I think of them now, they are bright green, that green of good summers.

Middlefield is a place like many others, where discordant realities can co-exist because of these soft external and unpredictable hills. Even though sometimes I wish they were mountains. It's a place where what you see depends on who you are. Where people are too fat and too thin in equal numbers, where there aren't enough labor unions or Democrats, where even now there are Donald Trump signs and maybe those signs will be up forever, where corn tastes better than it does anywhere else, where tomatoes taste red, where children don't know what to do in life because they have no role models, no paths, not many alternatives, where food pantries are enormous and quickly emptied, where what we all believe is wildly different, where sometimes that difference matters and sometimes it doesn't.

We are a family made by place, a family not by blood, not because of ancestry or immigration patterns, not because of any particular religion or intellectual proclivity, we are not all in book groups, we do not all fish or farm or read the same newspaper, we do not vote the same or dream the same either.

I never found a place I wanted to be until Middlefield. I never consciously thought about staying put. I am a theoretical wanderer, child of the seventies. I have never been to India or Bhutan or Tanzania or Nepal but I want to go. I've wanted to go for years. I am one of those vague women with vague ideas about politics, about art, about daily life, marriage, the Supreme Court, even religion.

I thought I understood right and wrong and why people did what they did until we came to live here. Until we had no choice but to live together.

PEGGY DOES NAILS

Nails are popular
in upstate New York and even
in the bigger towns nearby.
9,000 residents, three
nail parlors. The owners
are from Vietnam.
The woman at the desk,
she calls herself Peggy,
Peggy from Vietnam, comes
over to talk. Married a soldier
when she was a doctor.
"Real doctor," Peggy says.
She and the soldier
moved to the country and after
a while he faded away.
"Do you know the word faded?"
Peggy asks.
"I learned it yesterday."

DELORES

Delores, one of my favorite
people ever, not a sufficient description
Delores doesn't mind her missing
body parts:
thyroid, appendix, teeth, one kidney,
she's okay about various diseases
and all her doctors, some good looking.
She looked beautiful at dinner,
new silver shoes.
She said, "Sometimes I don't feel
all that good
but then I wake up to birds."
She has a married lover
named Ed. They can't
go out to dinner because
Ed has a wife, even though
they live 140 miles away.
Delores said Ed
is very careful, but she
brought Ed over
for dinner at our house
on a Saturday night.
We all liked Ed.
No one mentioned his wife.
Delores said the story
with Ed and his wife
is the usual story:
they've lived separately
for 22 years.
Not in the same room.
She said Ed's wife believes

the kids don't know,
that they would be upset.
The kids are in their forties.
Delores said, "They're probably
living separately from their
spouses too. It's a gene."
Delores is not in love with Ed.
She's been in love,
more than once. She met Ed
at a dance.
He was with a friend of his
and they started talking.
"That's all it takes," she said.
She's glad about Ed, "Because
every single Friday, rain or shine,"
Delores says,
"Ed is there at my door
with flowers in his hands."

Tom and Jane

Tom and Jane—Republican couple from Western New Jersey, a small prosperous town with horses, Talbots, expensive old bar with $22 hamburgers called Olde Sheffield Inn for no good reason—when they turned 70, they decided to sell their perfect New Jersey Federal home.

Their home was clean, well-curated, years of striven-for home décor perfection, the very same green their ancestors used, expensive milk-based paint. They had antiques and lifetime accumulations, no chips or visible imperfections, teapots and cruet sets, porcelain creamers, priceless quilts, and butter knives for twelve, though they never had twelve people eating butter all at once, but had that happened, the butter would have been in rosettes from their British wooden rosette set.

They decided to sell whatever they could and start over again in upstate New York, in a small town they didn't know. They picked upstate New York because they'd both been art history majors in college at the University of Iowa, and the Hudson River style of painting was the painting they felt most suited their sensibilities: broad vistas and a glory that was no more. One of their favorite writers, Edith Wharton, had lived in the Berkshires not too far away. They didn't want to live in the Berkshires for the very reasons that everyone else wanted to: they'd been discovered—Tanglewood and Jacob's Pillow and Big Culture a la Yo-Yo Ma. Although they were not adventuresome types, not discoverers either, not at all, this move was their first semi-calculated adventure. Two children, grown, both in San Francisco, were working and fine. They were free to move.

Their realtor used perfect Garamond typeface in her ad. Garamond was their favorite font. That's why they chose her. She also used the word *evoked*. *Upstate New York*, said Margaret Riley in her real estate ad, an ad they felt was written just for them, *evoked the Hudson River School*. Lush, mysterious, even magical: Olmstead, Thomas Cole, Frederick Church. The incomparable Hudson River.

They called Margaret Riley and she could not have been more polite. Almost gracious. Not very realtor-like. "Certainly," she said. And "But of course."

Margaret drove them around in her cheerful green Honda chattering in a pleasant manner, familiar but not overly so. She knew to keep her distance. Both Tom and Jane had the ability to chatter right back. Innocuous, pleasant enough, what the weather was now, what the weather had been, how they felt about New Jersey (they liked it). No politics because these days you just don't know.

"What are you guys looking for?" Margaret asked, and Jane, who fancied herself an amateur grammarian, did not say We Aren't Guys, although she wanted to.

Tom was more easy going. "We're looking for a change," he replied. "Another chapter. Not yet written."

"What are you looking for in a house?"

Margaret was a professional.

Everyone had an opinion.

"Mood," said Jane.

"Land," said Tom. "We like to garden. I grow tomatoes. Jane likes flowers."

"A certain amount of privacy," Jane added.

"We like neighbors but we don't want them right on top of us," said Tom. "If possible we'd like not to see them from inside the house. The ideal situation would be some big beautiful trees between us. Old maples would be perfect."

He smiled. Tom was accustomed to getting what he wanted.

And Margaret, most of the time anyway, was used to saying *Yes*, to acting as though whatever the client wanted was absolutely possible. Even though she sometimes knew that there was no way in hell they would find their dream home. Most people settled, just like they did in the rest of their life. Eventually.

So they continued, driving around together half a dozen times, familiar enough with one another. No need to tell them more than what they asked. One afternoon in October—when leaves can be orange and red, when days in upstate New York are beyond beautiful—one Thursday, actually the 9th of October, the day before Tom would be 71, Margaret drove Jane and Tom in her clean green Honda to a town called Glens Falls. And she pulled up to an old brick house, 1781, and Jane who was not given to much praise, more withholding than not, although her demeanor said otherwise, Jane said: "Almost Perfect."

"From the outside anyway," she felt compelled to qualify.

"You don't need the almost," Tom laughed. "I can actually see us living here." And he smiled. Tom was an easy smiler. His was a well-cared-for mouth.

"So can I," said Margaret although she knew, actually, that neither Tom nor Jane thought hers was a relevant vote.

Margaret had been selling houses for twenty-one years. Ever since her first husband left. Larry was a man she met in a bar. He was a master darter, won every single bar dart game for fourteen years without anyone coming close. Darts was who he was and what he was known for, far and wide.

When he was beaten by a younger man named Will McSweeney, whose name he never allowed to be said in his house after the inconceivable defeat, Larry never played darts again.

Margaret was taken by surprise, she really was, when Larry walked right out the door after eight years without warning, to live with her best friend Pat. Turns out Pat was a master darter too. Not that their marriage had been great. Margaret had two small children then. Working part time at a daycare center, she made very little money. Larry earned a good living as a union plumber, but when he walked right out the door, he took his money with him. Child and support were two words he pretended not to know. She went to court. He Officially Agreed. But payments rarely came. So she got her real estate license.

Driving around with strangers looking at houses suited her. After a little while, she sold her first house, an easy 50's ranch, clean and ready, half an acre, big enough for a Home Depot barbecue, to a young family with two small children happy to have a place of their own, for $139,000. Mortgages were easy to get in the poor upstate county where Margaret lived and she was glad to sell and glad to help. And once in a while, the people she drove around, people she sometimes found houses for, actually became friends. For example the first couple, because they knew no one in upstate New York (they were from Sunnyside, Queens), invited Margaret for dinner and they stayed in touch.

She became accustomed to driving very different types of people around the countryside. Families of firemen from Staten Island, Brooklyn hipsters with a baby named Una, retired schoolteachers ready for a life change, single women who'd always lived in apartments and wanted gardens with tomatoes and flowers and herbs. Margaret herself was born in Brooklyn when Brooklyn was not a destination, when working people lived in neighborhoods surrounded by people just like them.

She met Larry, and—the way people do when they are young, when they don't know much, when they don't understand the word "implication"—they'd moved in right away. They'd actually gotten together on the basis of bar drinks and a certain amount of attraction. He had a job, and seemed good enough. Her parents hadn't been a happy couple. Her father drank, her mother suffered, and nothing was ever going to change in their equation. Margaret herself liked to party well enough. Hers was a beautiful smile. Her hair was almost blonde, and her body, the body so many have when we are young, when we believe we will always be young, her body, never thin, was supple and strong. Margaret got sadder over the years, and wider too, but her beautiful smile was still right there.

Tom and Jane went back a few times with Margaret to look at the house. Once they brought an architect, a family friend Tom told her on the phone, someone who knew what he was looking at and how to make it better. He wore a light linen suit on their final house walk through. He pronounced the house ridden with potential. "We can do a lot here," were his exact words. After they bought the house and after the architect had made the changes they'd all decided were absolutely necessary—granite kitchen counters, for one—they invited Margaret over to thank her for her help. They served tea in a flowered English pot. The teacups, too, were part of the set. "We want to thank you," Tom said, and Jane smiled too, as though she agreed.

"My pleasure," said Margaret. They never saw each other again.

Am I Right?

Paul works at the post office
one of those
"Is that a joke? Yes it is"
sense of humor.
Married a few times
he's very very big
likeable even though
his politics
are not.
Last week when I went in
to buy stamps he said,
"I've got a sheet
of Jimi Hendrix for you.
You wouldn't know this just
by looking,"said Paul,
"but I know my customers.
Tom over the hill
would rather be dead
than put a Jimi
on his electric bill.
Not you," he said.
"Am I right?"

ANASTASIA

THE BOYS WERE BABIES, and they were mostly playing, every summer, in one of those big round plastic supermarket pools, with circus polka dots and puffy sides right on the grass under the big Black Locust tree, a Harry Potter tree that sits on top of a small rill (yes it is really a rill and we don't live in England or Ireland. Just upstate New York). They each loved water. Still do. They could sit in the big metal sink in the kitchen—thrown out by a Chinese restaurant in our neighborhood, one of those Big Woks, and just play with water for hours. I'd get lost in watching them.

Nick was on the road, playing with his band anywhere they could. Manuel, my oldest friend Manuel, spent days and nights in the fields. He could garden for many hours, sitting in the earth, not on top the way some people do. He'd become part of the earth itself. What he loved most was submerging his hands into soil. That was his work, how he earned his living. What he did the rest of the year mattered so much less. He didn't want to be a professional gardener. Landscaper either. He just wanted to plant for himself. What he put into the earth was his whole life.

When Alex was with us, a thin dry sweet labor historian, Alex spent his days and his nights reading on the porch. He read the newspaper very thoroughly. He read books, big books about historical figures: John Adams, Robert Caro, LBJ. He read *The Economist* and *The New Yorker* and anything else that came his way. He did not move off the porch very much, except to go to an occasional meeting of the upstate historical society.

I missed having a woman around, a woman to talk to. And I needed a little help in the house. I've never been a cleaner. I come from a long line of non-housekeepers. My mother, an oddly glamorous, distant, enigmatic card-playing chain-smoking non-maternal mother, never held a broom or an iron in her hand. In fact I got a call one day, a surprising call from her neighbor, Mrs. Keller. She never called before or after.

"Something's wrong with your mother," she said. "I saw her standing out in front of the house holding a broom in her right hand. 'Tillie,' I said, thinking about it for a minute. 'Do you want one of Walter's canes?' Walter had Parkinson's, and he couldn't walk at all in the end. I saved all his canes for no good reason. Your mother didn't say yes and she didn't say no, but I knew that was the only explanation for the broom."

My grandmother, too, a red-lipsticked card player, wasn't much for brooms. She did iron once in a while. I remember she owned an iron. But I never actually saw it moving over a piece of cloth. Me too, about irons and brooms. Still I want the space where I live to be a certain way. Maybe that's the reason, and maybe not, why I called the number on *The Pennysaver* for a woman who cleans. *The Pennysaver* is the free local Bible full of classified ads and new testament quotes. It's delivered weekly by someone driving by in a station wagon, throwing them out of his truck, flinging them right onto the driveway. I read ads for refrigerators as though they were poems. *The Pennysaver* was always completely unexpected.

Anastasia walked into our house, and she went right for the tea kettle. She had tea bags in her handbag, her favorite, she said, from Ireland. They were tied in a beautiful white linen handkerchief. She went every year, she said. She brought over tea for us both. "I've got enough for a few more," she said, "if there's anyone else you'd like to invite over." The boys were napping on the porch, so she made us tea and sat right down. I would have hired her right there.

"I guess you want to hear a little bit about my qualifications," she said. Anastasia is Vanessa Redgrave beautiful. White white white skin and eyes a color of blue that's hard to find in nature. She has one of those Irish voices you hear in good dreams. For someone like me, in love with James Joyce since I read my first Joyce sentence, she is the perfect person to sit on the porch with me. I didn't care whether or not she cleaned.

Still, that's exactly how she began.

"There's nothing on God's earth that I can't make shine," she said, and then she looked around us, all around us. "It's so beautiful here. My job should be easy." That's all she said about cleaning. It was easy for her to launch right into the story of who she was, who she'd like to be. "I see you've got two sons," she said. "I've got ten of them. They're all grown up now. Nothing's easy."

The first day we met, Anastasia wore a linen dress, the natural color linen that's the most beautiful. Not white and not beige. It made her skin look even whiter. Ageless, she looked as though she'd lived a big life and was continuing on that path.

Anastasia came from somewhere else. Born in County Kerry, she was the second child of eight. "My father," she said, that first day we met, "used to dig a long trench and fill it with a bed of hay for his potatoes to keep them good for winter. The trench was outside, from our house to the barn. We had so many people to feed. He made a beautiful stone fire outside with stones he'd gathered from all around the fields—it was as beautiful an outdoor fire as any I'd ever seen. He'd roast potatoes on that fire on top of an iron grate he made."

Anastasia wanted more relatives, people she chose, relatives who made things with their hands like potato troughs and stone fireplaces, like her father. Why that's what she wanted was probably as simple as this: because it was nothing like her indoors family of origin, thin and shy people who did not venture up mountains or down into ravines. They were practical more than romantic: doctor, lawyer, merchant, chief. They walked across sidewalks. They did not follow secret drum beats or listen to healers. What science and the self could do was what they most believed.

"I love to clean, by the way," said Anastasia. "I bring my own products. I have the perfect metal polish for your trays."

She talked, and I listened. Although people who do not know me well always assume the opposite—I am a real talker—there is nothing I like more than listening. Anastasia was a perfect match. She talked and talked, in her soft broad, all life is a story lilt. It took me many years to know that many of the stories she told me were made up. Of course I hired her right then. And right then, she became a part of our life. For more or less forever.

ALICE DOWN THE ROAD

"Come on in," said Alice,
as though she'd asked this a thousand
times before; but this was her first
invitation in 31 years, so I walked in.
"Sit down," she said and she pointed me
to where I should sit a yellow Barcalounger
facing the big TV. She sat on the matching
yellow couch. "My husband and I
are on that wall," she said.
"Do you remember him?
No good sonofabitch but he had some
good points. A cop for 29 years. Over there's
my daughter who died. Don't ask what year.
The other one's on my dresser. She's 63.
Never married. Why bother," she said.
"Before you go let me show you my kitchen."

Margaret and Constance

While she was cleaning Margaret said,
Constance won't go out with Jim again
mainly because she doesn't like his shirts,
although there are other reasons
and he's not open to changing them.
They can be frayed they can be less
than they should be." A man she dates
should have nice shirts, Constance told Margaret.
"Reason two," she said, "was that
when they last went out to dinner—
they are both 79 and like prime rib –
Jim makes good money selling insurance;
Constance still works in a school
as an administrator, she likes the word
administrator, says it often,
Jim has much more money than Constance—
no family, none even though he's Irish,
he's been divorced forever—
he asked her to split the prime rib bill.
As if shirts weren't reason enough."

Don't Come Here Now You're Not Welcome

MAY, WIFE OF JIMMY, the plumber, is how she introduced herself to strangers, even to people whom she'd run into at the supermarket whom she vaguely knew. May was on the other team from the people with Second Homes. Liberals, all of them, or Democrats at the very least, a Socialist or two in the mix, well intentioned Jewish or Unitarian or lapsed Catholics or Ethical Culturists. They'd been to college, had *helping* jobs: teacher, social worker, doctor, nurse.

May went to a Baptist Church a few towns away, although she was born Catholic, born into a family of Brooklyn Italians, big family where every single person, men included, knew how to cook a good meal. Her father was born in Calabria, and he was the best cook of all. Every Sunday, he'd make a meal, and relatives would cram into their small apartment in Bensonhurst and eat and eat and eat. May met Jimmy at her best friend Donna's wedding at Leonard's in Long Island in 1983. Donna was a hairdresser before there was the word stylist. She'd practiced on her mother, teasing her mother's hair out into a cotton candy pouf throughout her childhood, always playing with styles. Donna married Denny, and Jimmy was Denny's best friend.

Jimmy asked May to dance at the wedding. Although he was short, a little lumpy even, although his hair was too long, he was a good dancer, better than good even, and May felt happy enough in his arms. Before long, maybe six weeks or so, they were talking every day and seeing one another on both Friday and Saturday nights. May was working as a receptionist for a dentist named Wilson in downtown Brooklyn. Jimmy was a plumbing apprentice then. Always good with his hands, he used them to build things, and spent his weekends at the hardware store. Projects his middle name. When he proposed—which he did at Peter Lugar's steakhouse, a splurge for them both—when he proposed and said Let's Move Upstate and Have a Family, May said, "Yes," without knowing anything at all about life outside of Brooklyn. She said Yes and started planning their wedding: white dress, big cake, hall near her house that they could rent for a reasonable fee. One hundred twenty-six people, and after the wedding, after the Niagara Falls honeymoon where they ate pancakes and French Toast and steak for dinner every night, they spent their weekends driving from Brooklyn to upstate New York looking looking looking for a house. They rarely stayed overnight.

Jimmy was looking for a Big Project, and May wanted what she'd wanted since she was a young girl: a home and kids and a life inside. She wanted a 50's life, before women went to work, before having children wasn't considered enough. That was fine with Jimmy too. His was a traditional Italian mother. She even ironed his underwear. May and Jimmy lived the life they'd each wanted. Did what they thought was right according to their families, their church, and every single relative. Their life was good enough. Ordered. Predictable. Nothing changed except seasons, until neighbors moved in from Jersey City.

Not hippies exactly. Hippies seemed long ago. But people, four people, living together in some way that wasn't all that obvious, in relationships that were hard to see clearly from outside. No Mother Father boy girl dog. Four of them, two men and a couple. Sometimes a fifth woman came to join them. They bought the house next door in early October, when the light was still summer. May and Jimmy had a very neat house, all on one floor, a family ranch with an attached garage and a big sliding door. Their patch of lawn, always cut; flowers planted in rows. There were tomatoes in the back yard, and cucumbers, and enough zucchini to give some to neighbors, and a red Home Depot picnic table next to a round barbecue for hamburgers and other red meat.

The people next door bought more of a ramshackle house, an eyesore in May's opinion, with half-off shutters and peeling paint. She'd never be caught dead in a house like that, a house you could clean forever and still it would not have the possibility of being truly clean. She watched them as they came and went, arriving each Friday night from New Jersey with bags and bags, too many, it seemed, for one weekend.

She did not bring them a welcoming pie. She did not walk over to say hello. What she did was surreptitiously watch. Somehow they looked messy. Their clothes were a little too loose, and if she had to guess, she'd say they came from Goodwill. *Probably some idea of cool,* she thought. *But was 'cool' even a word these days?* If she had to guess, she'd say they smelled like that awful patchouli oil. There was a boy named Bob Kaufman in her big high school in Brooklyn who said he wanted to be a poet. He wore plaid shirts, and someone, maybe her best friend Donna, someone said he bought his shirts at Goodwill. She couldn't imagine why. She remembered he used the word *fuck* in a poem. She didn't remember one other word he wrote. Just fuck. The neighbors reminded her of Bob Kaufman. May had a good figure still, even after two children. Her clothes fit her trim body. Never did she look slovenly or loose. She was neat. Even in the morning when she served the family breakfast. Nearly always eggs: fried, scrambled, even poached. Jimmy had a beer belly, but he, too, was neat. His tools were always lined up in his toolbox, and you could literally eat dinner off the floor in his shop. Not that they ever did.

May read Nora Roberts pretty much non-stop. If she was a character in a Nora Roberts novel, she would fall in love with one of the men next door—not the gay men, hopefully, but that too was a Roberts possibility. The straight man, the one with the girlfriend, seemed more likely. He even seemed to play the guitar. She heard him sometimes, sitting on the porch playing old Beatles songs. She never liked the Beatles much. Didn't understand why other people did. Other people and their tastes were always a big puzzle.

Once, the neighbors came by and invited the whole family to a barbecue. They seemed unnaturally cheerful, walking up and down the street inviting every single neighbor as though they were all the same, whoever they could. Jimmy said maybe they should go, but May insisted they stay at home. The kids have colds is, what she said, even though it was summer, and the kids were constantly outside where anyone could see them. She didn't want to be involved with them, didn't like something about them. Although, she was polite. Able to talk about the weather for a minute or two if talking seemed necessary.

After the Presidential election in 2016, when May and Jimmy put up Trump signs and the Jersey City weekenders Hillary, May felt she didn't even want to say hello. *Hillary* she thought to herself. *How could they? Electing a Clinton after all that. How could they?* Jimmy wasn't a political man, and he didn't like watching the news very much. Sports yes. Always sports.

But May kept herself informed. FOX was always on in her house, and she believed she knew, in a very real way, what life was truly about.

When she heard about the pandemic years later, about how many people in New York City were infected, she thought at first—although this was not a thought she was proud of, she was from Brooklyn after all—that they deserved it, those people who did not follow the rules, who lived any way they wanted. Her next thought was they'd come upstate and bring the pandemic with them. She found a piece of poster board and made a big sign: *New Yorkers Stay Home* and put it right in their front yard, but Jimmy, not a man of compromise, not a man of moderation either, took it down when he came home from work.

"We're New Yorkers, all of us," he said.

"You know what I mean," May countered. "I mean them, not us," she said.

"What if we were them?" he asked. "Coming from Brooklyn to escape the virus. What if we were them?"

"How can you even say that?" May was rarely angry at him. And now she was.

"Maybe we're less different than you think," was all he said. But the sign didn't go back outside.

Irene at the Post Office

1

"You won't believe this,"
Irene often begins. She is 81.
We always believe her.
She restates when necessary
for absolute emphasis.
"Last night," she said,
"I went out
with a new man named Jim
and he offered to pay
but I said, 'no you don't
have to pay for me,
I'm a working girl.' And we
went to dinner at that
nice new place in Albany
all the way on the other side
of town. Afterwards,
when we got home
he said, "let me come inside,"'
she told all of us in the post office
hanging on for more,
"'No way,' I said.
'This is date number one.
A girl's got her rules.
Three,'" she said.
"'Three's your lucky number.'"

2

There is a writer named Lucy
"All writers should be named Lucy,"
said Irene at the post office.

Lucy lives on a hill
a white writerly house
well-perched, overlooking
purple and yellow fields.
"They must be wildflowers," Irene said.
Two days ago when she picked up her mail
Lucy said she was either dying
or she had severe indigestion.
Holly her partner took her to the hospital
half an hour away. "We have to
take out your appendix,"
the doctor told her. Lucy said,
"Can you take out
my Table of Contents instead?"

3

Irene wrote a big sign
next to her desk: *I will*
never give you mail if you
lost your key. Buy another one.
It's four dollars.
Just give me the money.
I'll give you the key.
That's the only way
you'll get your mail.
As always I lost the key
so I gave her four dollars
and she handed me a hardware sale
flyer along with my key.
"Have a nice day," she said.

SUE

She died a few years ago; we celebrate her birthday
each July. She would drive over here many nights
when Eli was very young, when we were alone
in the house during the week; everyone else would arrive
on weekends. Sue would drive over with a grandchild
or two or three, a bottle of wine.
She couldn't believe we had
Only One Child. Sue had ten, infinite subject matter,
always Doing Something. So was Sue.
Married a few times, had a boyfriend for a while; he was
young she said, he had Energy. She took care of
Alzheimer's patients; some had been famous once,
they couldn't remember. Sue sang to them.
Once she had an Alzheimer's Fourth of July barbecue.
A guest put her hamburger into her navy-blue clutch
for later, Sue said. When I think of summer
I think of Sue. How she would visit so many
nights and with her beautiful Irish accent she'd
sit right down, begin.

Where the View Is

Cheesy bar in a mountaintop
rundown old hotel, the kind I've liked
forever, five state view,
sometimes we name them,
off-key singer.
we order drinks, fried mushrooms
and then Hasidic family appears
from nowhere.
Jews are not omnipresent here.
Eight children and their mother,
they want to see the view. "Look
at all those states," the mother says.
Waitress, a thin woman
hair the color of Clairol Red
points to them and yells:
"The view is over there."

On the Verge

Marguerite O'Connell du Boisette, her name being far more evocative than she was, short, even squat, dark, wide and knotty, she always felt herself to be on the verge. For years, she was on the verge of a discovery: a life changing poem, a painting that would finally make her a painter, a lover who would know how to really truly love her, a job where her talents, hidden and mysterious, would float to the top of each day, an apartment where the sunlight she knew existed would finally stream into the windows, a mother who would love her with the unconditional love she deserved, a dress, velvet or satin or silk, so flattering her buried hidden beauty would finally emerge at last.

Her name was from a father who'd left. Her mother, Katherine O'Connell du Boisette of Queens forever, met a French painter in one of those odd coincidences. They'd both been at Jones Beach buying orange sodas. They were so young their differences didn't matter. He married her on a whim. Flamboyant, mustachioed, hairy and dark, he was happy, and so was she for the year they spent together. Then Marguerite was born. Katherine wanted to call the baby Daisy, but Pierre transformed her Daisy into Marguerite.

After the baby was born, they were happy for a while. They went on picnics and camped. The baby slept. She smiled. Then, one day as quickly as he'd appeared, Pierre just went away. Katherine kept his picture, and he stayed young as she grew tired, grey, and drained from the thought that whatever joy she'd had with him was simply gone.

Marguerite never thought to look for her father, even when she traveled once on a Eurail pass through France. She accepted his absence as part of her life, accepted that she'd always be without him. Still, she really believed that one day when she was forty, even fifty or sixty, her picture would change.

Her jobs were dull, her life was dull, and then her aunt Anne from Brooklyn suddenly died and left Marguerite and Katherine, her mother, money in her will.

Marguerite and Katherine were living separately. Their apartments were in Sunnyside, small and similar. Both apartments smelled like fried eggs though neither woman understood why.

They had dinner together every Thursday night. Marguerite rarely had somewhere else to go on Fridays, but she liked to keep them open just in case. On occasion, several times a year, a man would ask her to dinner. But she'd never see him a second time. She was sad, reserved and strange, not good at the banter men often required.

Week after week, Marguerite and Katherine talked about their money. Never before had anything so consumed them. They could leave the city, move to the country somewhere and start all over again. A bed and breakfast, even a motel.

They bought an old tan Toyota from a cousin and spent months of weekends, looking. Marguerite was encouraged by their trips. Her mother, never cheerful, nearly was. They dressed carefully, ate lunch in diners and small kitchens by the road and very often enjoyed themselves.

Finally, they happened upon the tiny village of Middlefield, and along an old river that ran through town, they found an abandoned motel. The rooms were small, but the floors were good and so were the walls and the roof. They could live in separate rooms if they liked. All the rooms had small refrigerators and stoves, a table and two chairs, and a surprising amount of sunlight.

It took them a week to leave two lifetimes. Marguerite's boss at the cheese shop shook her head with quiet disapproval, Katherine's supervisor at the glove manufacturer downtown where she'd spent nearly thirty years said a perfunctory good-bye. They left their jobs happier than either of them had felt in years.

By September, they'd moved to Middlefield. They bought every cleaning supply they saw, even bluing to wash old sheets, and they set out to build something for the first time either one could remember. Their mood stayed good for days. Katherine remembered all the words to "You Are My Sunshine." Marguerite, for reasons unknown, began humming on a regular basis the words to "I'm a Little Tea Pot." Sometimes, washing a floor together or a bathroom, they'd sing together. Usually, their duet was "When the Saints Go Marching In." They'd just start singing and never question why.

At night, they took turns making one another dinners—pork chops, hamburgers, even chicken a la king. And desserts, something neither ever made alone, Jell-O with fruit floating through it like fish, and velvety puddings, frosted cakes, fresh fruit pies each weekend. They both looked better, pretty and happy, almost different people, and they weren't altogether surprised at how much easier they got along.

One day, they decided they were ready for guests, so Marguerite painted a sign saying Guests Welcome and Wanted at Casa Marguerite. After forty-eight hours, their first family came. They were tired from traveling and seemed happy with the rooms they saw. Marguerite and Katherine gave them homemade chocolate chip cookies and milk.

More guests came quickly: firemen, friends from Staten Island, a man who taught high school art, two sisters on vacation, a guidance counselor from Western Pennsylvania. They came in waves: an aunt and her nephew, two overweight brothers from Winnipeg, a mother and her son. The women were busier than either one had ever been before. They cooked; they cleaned; they put flowers in vases for guests and themselves; they made the strangers comfortable. They even began to practice a show, a mother and daughter singing act with all their favorite songs. Every other Thursday during the summer, if it wasn't buggy or raining, they invited their guests to sing with them near a big sycamore tree in their yard.

The years went by far more happily than they could have imagined. The two became friends. They met people who sent them Christmas cards and came back again and again. Their singing got better. They sang encores. After a while, they sang rock and roll songs, though nothing very loud. The guests seemed pleased.

On her 45th birthday, Marguerite told her mother she'd always wanted a child. Her mother, who considered herself psychic, did not laugh at this. She thought it over very seriously before she said that 50 was when the baby would come. Marguerite accepted this.

The five years went by quickly. They painted the motel an unexpected red, not barnyard, but nail polish bright. They learned to make cherry tarts, homemade chocolate truffles, and fresh peach souffles. After a while, they started a small restaurant, Marguerite's Eats. The food was often good. Strangers assumed their life had been this pleasant for years.

One spring night two months before Marguerite's 50th birthday, so cold and clear the air still seemed frozen, Katherine and Marguerite took their evening walk. They felt a drop or two of rain. By the time they got home, it was pouring, a heavy relentless April shower. The drops looked pregnant, and Katherine and Marguerite ran home together, laughing at the way their clothes just clung to them. Katherine's old yellow house dress wrapped around her body like Saran, and Marguerite's loose purple print which reminded her of Hawaii stuck to her breasts and her stomach as though there was a reason why.

"Ominous," said Katherine, and both of them laughed all the way home.

Then Marguerite turned on the table lamp, and Katherine lit the fire under the tea and opened a box of shortbread.

"What will happen now?" Marguerite asked her mother, believing in her clairvoyance.

"Something," she replied. "Important," she added, smiling broadly.

Two days later, in another wild torrent, the women were eating pork chops and sauerkraut when they heard a knock so light it could have been a bird brushing alongside their door. But then it came again, a dry, sharp urgent rap. Marguerite went to the door. Her hair was off her face, held back by a white silk scarf she'd twisted into a headband. She looked very pretty, even young. A girl, very wet, stood in front of her. She whispered that she wanted to come in.

"Of course," Marguerite replied and smiled at her.

"My boyfriend, too," said the girl.

A man stood out from the bushes just then, a big man in a bright blue raincoat. His hood was on, and he was hard to see.

"We need a room," said the girl. "For a few days, anyway. Maybe even longer."

"Have some tea," Katherine suggested. "Would your boyfriend like some too?"

She motioned for him to come in, and he did. Older than the girl, he looked exhausted and uncomfortable. Their names were Barbara and Jim. She talked, and he nodded. She told the story of their vacation together. They planned on camping in the Adirondacks, but first their van broke down, and then their tent developed a mysterious tear. They couldn't fix it and were caught in the rain a few nights before. So they'd decided to stay in a room.

Marguerite thought there was something they weren't saying. She didn't think they were criminals, but she knew they were in trouble. They had an air of running away from something. But she didn't mention this to Katherine, and she went to bed wondering.

The next afternoon, she and Katherine were cleaning the rooms when they saw Barbara and Jim sitting in chairs on the lawn. Barbara was very pregnant. Her belly stuck up from the chair like a big round animal at rest. How had they missed it? Jim wore a bathing suit along with a T-shirt that said Rude Dog. He looked better in the daylight, a little less worried. Barbara's hair hung down around her face like a young girl's. She held onto a very fat book with a beautiful woman on the cover. She stared into the pages intently. Jim just looked out into the trees. He had a newspaper on the side of his chair, half-wrinkled. They kept to themselves. They cooked in their room and didn't talk much with the other guests. A week went by, then two. Marguerite wondered how long they'd stay. And what their story was.

One night they knocked on the door. It was Thursday. The women were eating their usual meal together, homemade rolls, fried chicken, fresh tomatoes and corn. They grew their own tomatoes, and spent every August canning sauce.

Katherine offered Barbara and Jim dinner. They both looked tired, not like they'd been on vacation. Everyone sat around the white enamel table with the kind of expectation that comes from sitting down with strangers. Katherine discussed her tomatoes. Jim said something about baseball. Marguerite asked if they liked to sing. Barbara replied in a soft, soft voice that what she liked to do was read.

It seemed like hours went by, though it may have been minutes. Finally, Barbara said, in a voice that was hard to hear, "I'm going to have this baby any day. Jim is married. He says he's going to get a divorce, but I'm only seventeen. We can't keep the baby. We just can't."

"I see," said Katherine. Jim stared down at the table as though it were a lake. Barbara talked to the women. Marguerite felt her heart stop. She couldn't breathe. Could this be her child?

"We want her to be happy," she continued. "With trees and flowers and a lot of birds. And tomato plants," she smiled.

"How do you know it's a girl?" Katherine asked; because she had been told that Marguerite was a boy by everyone who saw her.

"I talk to her," said Barbara. "I can tell. Jim has two boys anyway, so this one has to be a girl."

"What do you think, Jim?" She looked over at him but he didn't seem able to look up. "Jim," she continued. "He's worried," she explained. "He doesn't see any way out."

"We'll take her," Marguerite replied. "We've been waiting for a baby for a while."

Barbara and Jim looked at one another, and then at the two women. They all embraced in a circle around the old white table, and then Barbara and Marguerite cried. Katherine offered everyone champagne.

"To Celia," said Marguerite, who'd planned to use that name for many years.

A few days later, Barbara had a boy. They all named him Cyril. She and Jim left early the following day. As soon as they could, the women taught Cyril to sing.

What Happened to Phil

1

A neighbor named Phil lived
right across the street.
An Older Man, he said he shaved
every morning and every night.
He'd have a beard otherwise
and he didn't want to look like a Hippie.
Phil was tall enough, walked a little
like those big black bears. He loped.
He chain-smoked and carried two packs
at all times. One in his left-hand pants pocket,
the second rolled up tightly on the right arm
of his white T-shirt. He'd learned
that trick in the U.S. Navy. Classic tattoos:
Mother, and Milly, his longtime wife.
Small eyes, small lips, his nose most
substantial. Phil was not good looking
but he wasn't bad either. His voice
was full of cigarettes, scratchy
and low. "What's Doing?" was his hello.
He never waited to hear the answer.

2

Milly and Phil met in Brooklyn.
Seventeen and twenty. At O'Lunney's
Irish Bar. That was that, according to Milly.
She was in nursing school.
Phil drove a truck. A good union job.
Early on they decided they'd have
two children, move to the country

and work. Milly was energetic and thin.
She wore capris and gardened.
Baked good banana bread. Their daughter
and son grew up in the country.
Theirs was a quiet enough life.
Beer and cigarettes for Phil. Sports on TV.
Milly always cooked.
But life is never as simple as it seems.

3

One day the local police came right to their door.
Big and Not So Big Tom, police partners for years.
Phil and Milly knew them both.
Milly was sitting on her favorite rocking chair,
a chair that had once belonged to her Aunt May.
They'd called May a spinster.
Maybe she had been a liberated woman,
Milly didn't know for sure. Milly had loved May
and sat on the rocker as much as she could.
Phil was out in his truck when they came.
On Saturdays his pay was double.
Phil was a Teamster. He never went to meetings.
Milly was actually smoking a Newport.
She didn't smoke often. Just once in a while
to unwind. Phil did not object. She'd had a hard job.
She was a nurse in an understaffed Catholic hospital
in Albany. Never nurses enough, or time.
Milly smiled at the Toms. They did not smile back.

4

Tom Euell and Tom Dunne had been friends since
high school right there where they were. Now they were
policemen. One was tall and one was short. Twice a year

they and their wives socialized. Steak dinner out.
Tom Euell spoke more than Tom Dunne.
They were young, in their forties still.
Most of their job involved traffic tickets or alcohol.
Drunk speeding teenage boys.
That was mostly what they did.
Tom Euell looked at Milly, smoking nervously
in her aunt's oak chair. He asked her a question
although he knew the answer. "Phil home?" he asked.
His voice shook a little. Milly, who often felt worried,
felt more worried now. "He's working," she said.
"He gets double time."
"He isn't," said Tom with certainty.
"He's down at the police station.
We'll take you there."
"What happened?" Milly said. Her voice
had moved up several octaves. She could barely speak.
"Let him tell you himself," said Tom Number 2.

5

Milly got into the police car and she didn't know
what to say so she chain smoked and asked
about their families. So worried she didn't hear
their answers: various versions of Fine.
When they arrived at the police station on High Street
in downtown Catskill maybe fifteen minutes
from the house, it seemed like the car ride
took forever, when they arrived she got out of the car
forgetting her arthritis her bad right knee and
nearly ran into the station. Right there in a room
with buzzing fluorescent lights an awful yellow
a yellow that makes every single person look jaundiced,
as charged there in an innocuous molded chair

probably from the 70's, right there smoking a Pall Mall
as innocent as can be was Phil. Milly walked over
and he did not stand up. "What did you do?" she shouted.
"Nothing, absolutely nothing," he said.
She didn't believe him.

6

When they went home Phil didn't
look Milly in the eye. He usually did. She could tell
he was embarrassed. Not easily embarrassed,
he'd grown up on the South Bronx streets.
At that moment Milly wondered
if every single thing she knew about Phil
for all those years and years was a lie.
He was a gruff man with no soft side.
Never once had he given her flowers or any
jewelry either. Even a pin. Still she'd always
liked him. Maybe even loved him.
 "Now tell me," she said. She didn't feel as mad
as she'd been at the police station.
"What in the world did you do?"

7

Phil and Milly were sitting on their usual couch,
an innocuous blue, a little too light, made from
a material that was a blend of god knows what.
They sat right next to one another the way they always
did.
Both of them were smoking. Their bodies didn't touch.
A coffee table with a glass top and steel legs,
their idea of modern, sat right in front of them.
Two dishes of individually wrapped hard candies,
red and white mints and Planters dry roasted

salted peanuts were in the middle of the table
in their usual white bowls within easy reach.
Phil was not a talker. Not even under the most
talkative circumstances. Not a listener either.
More a presence,
one of those people who was just right there.
Who is this man? thought Milly.
There they were like strangers on the couch.
Not like a couple married 48 years.
They were nervous. They were unhappy. Unfamiliar
and familiar, both. After so many years
but there was so much they didn't know.
Milly was a competent person. A good nurse.
Phil knew trucks and roads inside out.
For once he took the conversational initiative.
He didn't do that often. "I copied Joe's credit card
in the Xerox machine and then I used it," he said.
Joe was his boss. They'd been friends
the way men can be and they didn't see one another
out of work very much. Once in a while
they'd have a drink if they were both on the road.
"Embezzlement," he said. "That's the word."
"I know the word," said Milly.
She read mysteries all the time.
What she liked when she read was plot.
"Joe wasn't the only one," Phil added, as though
this fact were just an afterthought.
"What in the world did you do with the money?"
Milly asked. She felt better somehow
knowing what happened.
"It was just a game," he said. "I did it because I could.
Never broke other rules. Not really. I'm going to be 73
this year and I wanted to break the rules at last.
I was wrong," he said.

"What will happen now?" Milly asked.
"How can we talk about this?"
"Talking's overrated," said Phil and then he actually
smiled at her. His smile was infrequent
so she smiled back.

8

Milly got up from the couch to walk to the kitchen.
She'd make food for them both the way she always did.
Phil was not a fussy eater. He was an old fashioned
meat and potatoes type. Whatever she put on his plate
he'd eat. She wanted to give him something.
To act as though everything was just the way
it had been before she heard he'd embezzled.
Before their whole life changed. She had minute steaks
and frozen French fries and Sarah Lee cheesecake.

9

Phil and Milly had two children.
Donna and Joey. They saw one another
at requisite times. Theirs was not a close family
and besides, each of them was married
to a so so spouse. Close was not their way.
They came and went when coming and going
was required.
Milly poured Phil a cup of black coffee.
She handed it to him in his usual brown mug.
"Do you think I should tell them?" she asked.
She didn't just call them out of the blue.
Every other Sunday morning for each of them.
Phil was not a telephone person.
He never got on the line. "There's not much
to say," he said. "If they send me away somewhere

then you'll have no choice." "Away," said Milly.
"This is a first offense. Isn't that how it works?"
"You watch too much Law and Order," said Phil.
"Life is not the same as your favorite TV show."
And for the first time in a while,
Milly actually laughed.

10

Phil didn't kill anyone he just embezzled
here and there not even enough money
to buy a new car and his boss who was his friend
forgave him in court and because he had an appealing
public defender a young woman named Ella,
recent CUNY law school graduate, first in her family
to go to college, from Puerto Rico, she wanted
to get him off because Phil was her first case,
she said. Phil is not the usual perpetrator, he's 72
and has two bad knees not just one,
and he didn't have a plan, big or small. Phil got off
with 60 hours of community service
and in the City Diner
after the trial where Phil took Milly for chicken
and waffles, he said, "I Swear I'll Never Do That Again,"
and she said, "I Certainly Hope You Don't."

Woman Came by Yesterday

She delivered a package from UPS.
We sat on chairs outside and she said,
"Tell me about yourself."
"Would you like to go first?" I asked
and she said, "OK. I'm a 49 year old
born again former actress," she said.
"Married a handsome minister.
Four children all grown.
The boy's a policeman but he acts
in a theater in Albany. Shakespeare.
Two of the girls are photographers.
They're single and take pictures
of weddings. The baby works
in the hospital in human resources.
I home-schooled all of them and now
I work for UPS.
What about you?
Do you want a day or two to think over
what you'd like me to know?"

NORA

NORA LIVES IN a small broken house up the road. When her first cousin Maria from Paterson, New Jersey, single with no heirs, left $15,000 to Nora, the first extra money she had in her long life, she bought a house, her first house, at seventy-four, in Middlefield.

When she walked down the road, trucks and cars would take notice. She was not the kind of person who usually walked down most roads. All her life she had lived in downtown Patterson, New Jersey. When she walked, she glided, she flowed. She did not meander. She did not strut or stride.

Hers was an unusual presence. It wasn't just a question of deportment. Taller than usual, maybe six feet even now, she towered. Her clothing, odd by any standards, loose and long and often frayed, covered her thin dramatic frame like an ancient toga. Her body, long and thin, was still in the good column. Good enough.

Nora called around to librarians in upstate towns asking if they knew cheap houses near the libraries. Robin, a well-read longtime librarian near Middlefield, told her about an old house, small and full of problems, but a real house anyway, that was, for various reasons, only $30,000.

Nora had always worked part-time, as an office assistant, as a waitress, as a babysitter, even though she didn't much like children. She read Euripides in Greek, spoke nine languages though she was often too paranoid to say what those languages were. She had a strong jaw, frequently wore a ragged caftan she'd bought 56 years ago on St. Mark's Place from Kwame, a Ghanaian vendor who became her occasional lover for a while.

She loved the theatre and could talk forever to strangers on subjects like What Makes Great Theater; why Edward Albee was better than Chekhov. They'd often walk away from her. She had strong opinions and didn't much care what the people she was talking to thought. For her, dialogue was an abstract idea when it wasn't in theater.

She'd been in Middlefield for nearly a year. And she surprised herself by liking it well enough. All she missed was an occasional lover. Possibilities in the town where she lived seemed entirely nonexistent. Her neighbors were generally kind. They sometimes dropped off food, soups and cookies, and an occasional pie.

One day Nora went to the post office, knowing Postmistress Irene was a guaranteed good audience. Irene knew how to listen. This made her very popular. Most people would come in and buy a stamp to talk. Martha was often sitting there too. Martha spent a few hours most days sitting on the post office chair. She'd bring her lunch— ham sandwich on white with no mustard or mayonnaise, a small bag of potato chips, and an old-fashioned thermos full of coffee with milk and plenty of sugar. Mostly she'd crochet square after square after square.

Nora never bought stamps, did not pick up her CVS flyers, did not use the post office except for occasional monologues several times a year. She entered the post office, small one room in a wooden building from the Fifties that also housed a one-bedroom apartment, an apartment that was called *transitional* even by Betty the real estate agent.

"You won't believe what happened to me," announced Nora.

Irene, a decorative postmistress, herself in her middle eighties, Irene who painted her eyebrows as though they were low flying birds; Irene, sociable woman well suited to the job of seeing the same people every day even though she did not like the postal part of sorting stamps, nor did she like making change, Irene said, "We are waiting." She even added, "with bated breath."

Martha, more dour than Irene, was crocheting yet another square—she had a whole room full of them, but that did not stop her from making more. All her squares were pale: pale blue pale pink pale yellow pale green. Martha herself was not pale at all. She looked tough and strong, actually ageless, big capable hands not well-suited for the delicate crochet hook.

"Ladies," Nora said. "Ladies," she repeated as though they could have possibly missed her declaration.

Irene smiled her usual good-natured 'Welcome to the Middlefield Post Office' smile. And Martha, not much of a smiler, nodded in Nora's direction.

"You won't believe what happened to me," Nora said again, her voice both low and loud.

The women looked at her as though they were watching something interesting on TV. "I was on a dating site," she continued, "called *Plenty of Fish*. It's free, and I don't have money. I met a man named Morris there who used to be a Beckett actor, and I am a Beckett fan. We seemed destined to meet."

Martha looked up from her crocheting and said in her loud, raspy voice: "Who is Beckett?"

"Samuel," Nora responded, her only explanation. Martha nodded, and Nora continued. "After 22 emails and a few long phone conversations, he invited me to meet him at the Day's Inn in downtown Albany for a three-day weekend. Not that we have weekends at our age. He said we would have separate rooms and he would pay for them both. He said he'd pay for everything. He'd been a member of the Screen Actors Guild and seemed to have quite a good pension. 'We will eat well,' he promised. 'We would drink wine every day, starting in the afternoon.' It's been years since I've had a weekend like that."

"Not true of me," said Irene, but Nora was not interested in hearing Irene on this subject. She was determined to continue.

"He had a good voice," said Nora, "and good voices are one of the things I look for in a man. If you've been trained in theater, and I have," she said, and paused to make sure that both women knew she wasn't just any ordinary person walking in the door for a stamp, "you know a good voice from bad. And Beckett was the cherry on top."

Irene, a kind person, said because she knew it was expected, "Please go on." She could tell, though, that Nora wanted more of a response from her, so she added, "I'm curious to know what happened. And so is Martha."

"Well," said Nora, "I asked my neighbor Frank to drive me to Albany. I offered to give him ten dollars for gas. He dropped me off at the Day's Inn, and I checked into the room right away. It was small but clean enough. And then, I waited and waited and waited for three days. And Morris didn't arrive. Waiting was horrible. I called him. I texted him. No answer at all. Had he vanished? Had he died? I was angry and worried and confused. None of these was an enviable state."

"Get to the end," said Martha.

"What happened?" Irene smiled patiently. "What's the rush Martha?" Irene said.

"Well," said Nora. "I never did hear from him. And I'm out $180 now. No more Morris. Maybe I imagined him all along. Anyway," she added, "just in case you're interested, I walked next door to a food co-op to buy myself an apple. I met a man named Feisel, who was an uber driver. Buying apples too. He drove me all the way home."

LINDA

Since Dick died last November
Linda's been mostly inside. Yesterday
she came out.
"My grandfather told me 55 years ago,
I was eight and knew I was in love with Dick,
my grandfather yelled,
'Don't you dare marry that boy!'
Dick and I knew one another 63 years.
I was six months old when we met
and he was four. Our mothers were friends.
He always made me laugh. Even in
the end when he was in hospice
and couldn't remember much he said,
'Let's get married again, Linda.
Have some more babies.'
'I don't have those parts any more,'
I told him. 'That doesn't matter,' he said.
'Let's just do it now and see what happens.'
And you know something?
We did."

PUZZLES

SHELDON WAS OUR NEIGHBOR and a stranger for our first ten years in Middlefield. A man you were ambivalent about to begin with, even on his best days.

Strangers often seem full of a kind of irrepressible urgency. They tell you it's now or never. Friends are the ones who are more apathetic, who choose to be sick the day you finally have a party, who are only somewhat interested in the intrigue of your daily life. It's strangers, with their smooth palms and thinnish eyebrows, who appear the most interested. At least at first.

Sheldon spoke with the lucidity of a mathematician, although he was part owner in a prestigious and obscure puzzle manufacturing company with the pretentious title of Palimpsest. The puzzles, he claimed, were opaque and difficult, only for knowledgeable and persistent puzzlers. No dogs playing poker around an oak table for Sheldon. No maps of New England or horses frolicking in open fields. His puzzles were mathematical equations, Oriental rugs from Tabriz. They were knowledgeable and intricate, but pretentious and expensive, very much like Sheldon.

He majored in drama at Yale. He read plays, and strongly preferred the Greeks. He read them in the original. He sneered at the idea of translations. Sheldon was loyal, though, and persistent. He was a dogged man. He pursued Leila with a serious consistency: every Tuesday morning he would call her, and holidays, he'd send presents to her apartment in New York City.

Small puzzles of Persian miniatures, Cyrillic alphabet puzzles that took her nearly a month.

What was odd was that she did them. She never just left them in a drawer.

Sheldon had a puzzle a month club, and he tried to fit the puzzle to the month, like fruit. In winter, he sent what he referred to as moments of solace: the musical score of Beethoven's "Pastoral," a Gaelic recipe for mutton stew. In spring, he was opulent; in summer, lush; and fall's puzzles, he entitled *Aftermath*. Sheldon had wanted to be a poet, really. He said he studied theater because he didn't have the courage for the truth. He called theater a profession of lies. Still he earned his living with visual poems. That's what he called his puzzles the first time he and Leila met.

She asked what he did—they were backed against the same wall at a very crowded party, and she was too tired to ask more than that. She hated the question as well as all the answers, hated the prejudice she had in advance for what he'd say. She knew that there were interesting investment bankers and dull cartoonists. Still, if someone said at a party that they worked on Wall Street, she knew she would excuse herself and just walk away. But if they said they drew cartoons, she would stand right there no matter how inarticulate they might be, no matter how difficult or odd. She would persist with them for no reason except the idea she had, that drawings were part of their everyday life. She knew perfectly well that artists were often dull.

Their apartments were generally full of nothing but their own work, one whole room, or two or three, of nothing but their paintings, their miniature boxes strewn with lips, their golden mummies or plaid violins. Anyone else's work, if it was allowed, would be hung in an obscure corner.

And writers were worse. They had other people's books of course, but they were usually full of disparagement about them. "Can you imagine that John Updike has a major reputation?" they'd say. "His sentences are so long. If he were unknown, he'd be blasted." Or, "Philip Roth wouldn't know a woman if he saw one." Investment bankers made no such remarks. They bought books and enjoyed them on vacations. They happily went to museums on Saturday afternoons. All the paintings they had were by strangers. They gave these strangers places of honor in their homes: over their desks, above their beds, in the center of their living rooms. Leila knew this. Even so, she persisted in her prejudice, looking for art by looking for artists.

Leila herself was a poet. Her poems were only fair. She tried not to mention the sunlight or moons, or to use wind in any of her titles. She worked in an office for Poets in the Schools. She found other poets a little too pale, too fixated on sore throats and unhappy childhoods, their too-small apartments, and their cats.

Leila kept her distance. She smiled with what she hoped was a serious politeness. She rarely discussed her own poems, though she often submitted them to publications with titles like *Armageddon* and *Embers*, publications that sent her back form postcards saying, "We only read poems for ten days in March," or "Thank you for giving us the chance to read your poems." She never received a word of encouragement, never a handwritten note. She persisted, not because she thought she was good, but because being a poet was what she decided she'd wanted years before, the first time she memorized a poem:

Someday, Jane shall have, she hopes

Rainbows for her skipping ropes

These lines stayed with Leila even when, for a brief period in college, when she attempted to shake all that was not serious out of her system, all that was not universal or important. Once, she even wrote the poem on a piece of paper, then ripped it up into very small pieces. An exorcism. But it stayed.

"What do you do?" Sheldon had asked first.

"I work in an office," she said, not sure enough of him.

"Come on," he pressed.

"I write poems," she replied, as though she was saying too much.

"And you?" she asked.

"Well," he'd responded, as hesitant as she. "I am involved in a kind of visual poetics, myself."

And then he told her about the puzzles.

"Would you be interested in seeing one? I can arrange it."

She imagined him walking into a large room of puzzle packers.

"We have some concrete poetry," he said, pronouncing concrete to rhyme with coquette. "'The Apple Tree.' Maybe you know it. It's in German."

Why she agreed to see him, she didn't know. He was only in the city for a very few days, and he invited her to dinner. She went, and in spite of his overblown ways, he could be interesting, even kind. They actually enjoyed themselves.

For their first dinner, Sheldon chose Tibetan food, spicy and cheap. Leila was pleased they weren't in a serious French restaurant, with an insistence on fresh pepper. The Tibetans served holy noodles, a funny yellow with shredded, indistinguishable vegetable sauce. And taro shrimp on the side, shrimp wrapped in something that tasted like a weird potato. Sheldon talked about how he came to puzzles, and why he'd moved to upper New York State. His cheeks were pink, and his way of breathing made him seem healthy. He seemed full of good will, like the kind of man who eats a big breakfast. His talk was easy and pleasant. He knew a lot about theater, and although he was disdainful of most attempts he saw, he said several times that he admired people who had the courage to try. He did not, he admitted, although he hoped he could change.

"Someday," he told her, as the gay Tibetan waiter brought their bright red tea, "I intend to leave upstate New York to live somewhere remote and beautiful like Micronesia or an island in the Caspian Sea. Of course, I'd like to take someone else with me. Someone with similar aims." He looked at Leila expectantly, as though she were in the running. And she, in spite of all her doubts, wanted to be. That's the way they began.

He sent her his first puzzle. It was a beautiful detail of an ancient Greek urn, a blue and white man running off the edge to something you couldn't quite see. Leila was moved when she put it together. There were never picture guides for any of Sheldon's puzzles, only the most elusive clues, usually in his titles. She sent him back a present too: a rice paper book from the Himalayas, with a beautiful cover of striped purple silk. He called her the following Tuesday to tell her how beautiful it was. That was their beginning, their first round of long and circumspect Tuesday morning calls.

Sheldon sent handwritten notes with his gifts, in writing so small Leila couldn't help but believe he'd read somewhere that there was a link between intelligence and handwriting size—the smaller, the better. Leila's own writing was a little too clear, too loopy. It bothered her, but she thought changing it would be false. She typed when she could, even to him. She tried to think of amusing stories to tell him. About being locked inside the bank foyer when her cash card wouldn't work, about her Aunt Sadie's married boyfriend whom Sadie taught to make stained glass, about all the things she forgot. Leila had a hard time remembering. She often confused dates and places. More than once, she'd shown up for a party the day before, or two days after.

She sometimes even forgot her own poems, and she read them, scattered around her apartment on pieces of paper, as though they were the words of strangers.

Sheldon himself was very precise. As precise as a puzzle. He courted Leila very slowly. As precise as he was, however, what he hoped for was not all that certain. He had no intention of tying his life to someone as chaotic as Leila seemed to be, and yet, he found himself inescapably dialing her number every Tuesday to hear her voice. She often sounded nasal, as though something in the air was giving her problems. He told her she had New York nose. Sheldon himself was carefully healthy. He did not eat dairy foods, did not drink coffee, and hadn't been near red meat for many years. When he saw a McDonald's, he turned his head away.

Leila ate everything. She loved McDonald's fries, and ketchup. She loved Coke in bottles and twinkies and devil dogs and ring dings and cupcakes and nuts. Anything overly sweet, or chocolatey, or fizzy. Sheldon was very disapproving of this. He said she had the tastes of a spoiled child. He sent her pamphlets on nutrition, articles clipped from *Prevention* and *The New England Journal of Medicine*, whole books about sugar and salt. She laughed at these, and on one Valentine's Day, she sent him the biggest box she could find of chocolate covered cherries. They rarely saw one another, meeting once or twice a year. Presents held them together. And when they met, the feeling between them was somewhere between passion and the casual friendship of ongoing business partners who do their business by phone. They knew one another well enough to spend three or four days going to theaters or museums, or eating cheap meals together.

Leila stayed in Sheldon's room whenever he came to town. His moderate but respectable hotel. She'd leave every morning for her own small apartment, and he would pick her up there later. They only made love in his hotel. At her house, Sheldon was nervous and polite.

Then Sheldon drove down on Valentine's Day. This was surprising. Sheldon was a careful romantic rather than a spontaneous one. He left a handmade puzzle at her door, which she found after work: *Will You Marry Me? I Am Waiting at the Mayflower.* The border of the puzzle was pale green circles, champagne grapes, each separately carved. She took a bath to consider. What did she really think of Sheldon? Then she dressed in velvet and Sheldon's favorite perfume. Four days later, they married. Leila wrote a poem about it called "The Puzzle," and Sheldon turned her poem into a puzzle with locking hands.

Maeve on County Route 17

We met Maeve through my friend Sheila.
Sheila didn't go to church but still
she knew priests, maybe from Ireland,
they were mostly from Ireland. Every single summer
she'd come over, talk about her husband,
her big big Irish family, arriving in Brooklyn.
Her husband Dennis died on Easter Sunday
his 89th birthday in hospice in Florida.
Maeve's sister, Bridey, called to tell us
Dennis died and I called Maeve to say
we were sorry. She said one of her happiest days
in her long life was when Ziggy a neighbor
took us in his truck for vegetables and ice cream.
"Do you remember what Ziggy
said after we ate the ice cream?" she asked.
"Now let's get some pie."

A Neighbor Whose Name I Don't Know

A neighbor whose name I don't know
walked into our field with a young boy
and a dog. "Can I help you?" I asked,
a euphemism for why are you walking
across our field?
"I'm beyond help," he replied,
smoking a cigarette. He actually looked
like help would be a good idea. "I'm Hava,"
I said."I'm Sam," said the boy. The man
did not reveal his name. "This is our field,"
I told him. "I know," he replied,
and that seemed to be the extent
of what was possible to say.
Yesterday when we were going to the store,
Nick said the man, the boy, and the dog
were in the field. "Are you implying
that we should do something?" I asked.
"Absolutely not," said Nick.
"Only adding to the information."

Lorraine Or Why Aren't You Here

I MET LORRAINE at CVS. I am a CVS regular, although I don't believe it's any different, even a hair, from Rite Aid or Walgreens or any other drugstore chain. CVS, in these mountains where we live, is an external destination of another kind of civilization. It's not just the products, many options for headbands and toothpaste, now even cookies, delicious CVS Macadamia nut chocolate chip really truly better than Pepperidge Farm.

I walk into the store, pick up a local paper—I still read the old-fashioned paper paper—and go right to the 75% off bin. CVS always has one. It's full of colors I want: many nail polishes in inconceivable shades (fig brown, elephant grey, neon green, and electric eel blue).

Lorraine was looking through the same bin one day. She's a woman in her sixties who hasn't lost her thing, that elusive she's-still-so-good-looking quality I'm sure she'll have for all her life. She said she likes unusual hair products, guava juice, and odd nut oils. CVS, she claimed, although it seemed counterintuitive, had a pretty big odd hair product range.

Although I am a regular, I'd never met anyone else in CVS before. Not anyone who'd said much more than *where's the soap?* Lorraine started talking as though we were old friends. There are people like that, people who can look right across at you and suddenly you become friends. I've had that experience a few times: strangers in a mutual context who seemed, for one reason or another, familiar enough to cross the boundary.

"Let's go have coffee," she said. "There's a Dunkin Donuts where we can sit outside and watch the cars go by. Al fresco," she said. "It's the best we can do around here."

We really are in the middle of nowhere. Not well-manicured intentional, or the Berkshires, or Columbia county with its myriad used bookstores, infinite copies of Edith Wharton. This is another nowhere: more real maybe, more Steinbeck than Wharton, more canned pickles than heritage tomatoes. Only the diner is open seven days, and eating out happens once in a while.

We both ordered the summer drink, one of those made up words like Lattichino. It could be real Italian, but it's probably Duncan Donutese. And then we took our drinks outside, to the lawn furniture facing the mild highway that passes through this area, punctuated by Stewarts and the Catskill Creek. A kind of upstate plastic William Sonoma. Somehow OK.

All around us a color that isn't quite green. Some years ago, there was a chain store, now no longer, that had a kind of lawn furniture now ubiquitous all over this part of upstate New York. It was one of those items, like screen doors and Coleman coolers, that caught on overnight. As a child I remember sitting in the same green and white plastic woven lawn chairs on all the lawns I visited. They had the possibility of reclining, and I heard the word recline many times in my seventh-grade summer. These chain store lawn chairs, not green or black but somewhere in between, oddly curlicued, metal like material that may or may not have been metal, made in China for sure, was what we all suddenly sat on.

"I'll start," said Lorraine, with an enthusiasm that seemed entirely real. "I'll tell you who I am. Then you can tell me back if you want." She smiled, a woman who has seen a lot or more than most of us.

Lorraine is pretty. She started out that way and always will be pretty. She's the sort of woman who always, no matter what happens, looks good, well-cared for, like someone who has options. Her clothing is fashionable enough, but not intimidating. Flattering, more than fashionable. The day we met, she was wearing a light blue gauzy Indian style shirt. Blue for her eyes.

"There are a lot of places where I can begin. I'll go with Long Island. I lived there, not far from Port Jefferson, for 40 years. Married my high school sweetheart. Steve. Four kids. All in a row. No hiatus for us. School, work. I became a nurse. Never-ending busy lives. Dogs and cats, kids and friends. We both worked, and every single day our lives were full. One day out of the blue, really, Steve turned 60. He issued an edict: 'I want to stop what I'm doing and do a little less. We need more time just for us.'

"We'd had a hard time finding the space to be alone. When the kids had their own kids, alone really became impossible. He suddenly wanted more room for us. More space, too. Me, I always enjoyed the chaos. I guess I liked being needed in that way. The whole mother-grandmother thing. Knowing that someone depended on me. Men are different. They just are. Anyone who says that isn't true is wrong.

"We'd been married nearly 40 years. Forty good years, I'd like to add." She paused here, then asked, "You?"

I knew what she wanted was the short version. So, what I said was, "Fifteen long years."

She continued, "'Let's move upstate,' he told me. 'We can live near your Aunt Bea. The kids can visit. What do you say? This is the time of our life to start over. Come on, Lorraine. Let's do it.'

"Steve's not the Let's Do It type. Not really. His life went right along on a kind of predictable path. He was a high school football player, and the boys he played with stayed his friends forever. He didn't veer off the path. Me neither.

"Aunt Bea is like the Wicked Witch of the West. My mother's sister. The rest of the family died years ago but not Bea. You can imagine what she's like. Never married. She says she never had that particular need. But her little house—she lives alone, and she's 92—faces onto the mountains, and there's nothing like just sitting there. Steve's liked it since we came up here to visit so many years ago."

I was listening to her story as intently as I could. Sometimes when people talk about their lives, I feel as though I'll never be able to forget one word they say. A psychiatrist told me, many years ago, that I listen as though I am deaf. That's how it feels.

"Before you could count to ten," she laughed, "here we were. Right here. We came up one weekend and bought a house. It really was that simple." She paused, as though it was time for me to say something. Anything. Maybe even ask a question.

"How'd you find a house that fast?"

"We got a copy of the *Pennysaver,* and there it was. "Mountain views. Energy efficient. Owner moving to Florida. Wood stove. Move in ready." That's what the ad said, and that's what we did. One of our daughters moved into our house on Long Island with her family. They were renting nearby, and the landlord was an old high school friend. The move could not have been easier. So there we were, and here we are. High school sweethearts," said Lorraine. "More happened, of course. When we meet next time," she said, "it's your turn."

CHRISTINE

Christine owned a clothing store
next door to the hardware store
in the nearby town.
Two girls stole their prom dresses
by putting them on and then walking
out the door.
Christine called the police.
Everyone went to the precinct
together. The girls' parents
chastised Christine
for ruining the prom.
A month later Christine moved
to Michigan.

BORN AGAIN PIANO

NICK AND I had grown up with pianos, and our Middlefield house had plenty of space, so I decided I wanted a piano for our home, a pounder for practice, to make our own music. Nick was the only one who regularly played an instrument. He's one of those people who can pick something up and just play: harmonica, accordion, oud, guitar. I'd played piano as a child, without much talent, but with a certain happiness at turning sounds to music. My piano teachers—there'd been three—were humorless and dour, especially my last teacher, a man named Harry (I loved his name, but that was all), who taught me for three years. All I remember was his weekly admonition: "Chopin entirely eludes you."

Harry did not think I had much chance to improve. He was adamant and convincing, and although once I tried the What About the Pleasure of Playing argument, I didn't get far. "You need proficiency for pleasure," was Harry's reply, and maybe because I was young, I didn't know any better.

Years intervened between me and pianos. Our New York apartment is just plain small: the rooms are full without a piano, so there was no chance. And we didn't want an ugly white keyboard, one of those plastic pieces that sounds like erasers and tin.

Our country house has space—it's not yet completely full with yard sale paraphernalia—my egg beater collection, for instance, takes up only half a kitchen wall. While there's still room this summer, I thought, I'll try to buy a piano.

My friend Igor, a trumpet player, has also a high-pressure, high-powered, high-paying job full of prestige and colitis. He decided to take it upon himself to devote a certain amount of daily computer time to my quest. Igor uncovered about half a dozen classifieds, here and there. None of the sellers of pianos seemed interested enough to call me back, and only one of six actually answered her phone. She was cranky and short.

"It's nine thousand dollars," was all she said.

She knew before I said a word that I was thinking more in the free-for-the-taking camp.

Then Igor met an unlikeable piano tuner. Igor played the trumpet very well, but he played piano too. The tuner wore a suit, his hair was short, and his favorite all-time composition was "Winter Wonderland." He had to be pressed extensively by Igor, who was a master of inquiry—the tuner did not like to give up any information at all, even his first name: his *Pennysaver* ad said, "Call Mr. Edge to fix your piano," except that his fixes were always dire piano-related diagnoses. Eventually, he said he knew of a piano: a protégé's family had bought a Yamaha.

Igor found out that the old piano was not only available, it was just one hundred dollars. He got me the number and I called.

Mr. Charles lived only two towns away. Mr. Charles, while he wasn't at all friendly (No *Oh Boy You Want to Play the Piano* in his tone), didn't slam the phone down, either. He confirmed his fee of one hundred dollars and said his piano was perfect. We made an appointment to look, and then, because there are no real street addresses in this part of the country—only fire route numbers, in case there's a fire—we went to the wrong house. The wrong house was on a funny curved street off Main in a little town nearby, a town with a supermarket, a hardware store, a library, and not much else—was charming, a little decrepit, and the man who came to the door, ageless, with a toupee sufficiently askew to give his head a certain rakishness; he introduced himself as Mr. Dawn. Nick and I both wished the piano had belonged to Mr. Dawn—his hands were gentle, his manner graceful.

"I love pianos," he said. "But I've never had one."

We found Mr. Charles, eventually, and he was far less welcoming. His porch was a porch where no one ever sat. Both old wicker chairs were missing their seats. It had that tacked on for no good reason feel. The first thing he said was that God had sent us to him to buy the piano. That was almost enough for Nick to leave. We didn't know quite what to say. I tried concentrating on his outfit: a white undershirt stretched tight across his belly, thrust forward in front of him. Loose and low. He wore old-fashioned Bermudas, held under his belly with a wide black rope. On his feet were black sneakers. Nothing was wrong really and yet everything was.

Inside, the house had the same disturbing quality as a Stephen King novel. Subtle creepiness, hard to pin down. A room with two pianos was very clean, very spare—a large copy of *The Holy Bible* sat on an old coffee table, in front of a plastic-covered couch. Everything looked grayish. No pictures, no magazines, no supermarket flyers lying around. Easy to picture a murder happening there. Mr. Charles shared his house with his protégé son George. He summoned George by calling out his name, just yelling into the air in a peculiar high-pitched way.

When George entered, he did so with the forcefulness of an angry cat. He was a tiny boy, and he too didn't seem at all glad to see us. "George is a piano genius," Mr. Charles told us. "But God wants him to be a politician instead. Meanwhile, he'll continue to play the piano. We've had piano presidents," he said, in a way that did not allow for us to ask him who they were. "Richard Nixon. Harry Truman. I think they're the most famous."

George sat down at his bench and *actually* scowled, ageless teenage boy demeanor. He was twelve at the time. Soft body. Indirect gaze. His hands were different, hard, and strong, and his technical skills were clear. When he played two Czerny Etudes, on command from his father, his fingers did not falter. We congratulated him on his impressive performance. Eyes looking down, he became a young boy again, mumbling, "Buy this piano" before he left.

Mr. Charles continued, "It's six hundred dollars," he said.

"You told me one hundred on the phone," I replied. He did not deny what he'd said. But that did not prevent him from repeating the words "six hundred dollars."

I didn't want the piano. Not even a little. Neither did Nick. It seemed cursed. Can a piano be under a spell? Is there such a thing as a born-again piano? We felt we should play it, anyway, before we left. So we sat down together and tried the simplest chopsticks. In our four hands, the piano became leaden. Keys stuck, and sounds didn't emerge when they should have. We stood up and Mr. Charles looked at us, disgusted. With us, not his piano.

"God doesn't believe this piano is yours," is all he said.

MOLLY COMES TO VISIT

Ex-girlfriend
of one of the Beatles
she won't say which one
we all think Ringo
hard to be sure
she is 70 and beautiful.
Maybe more
beautiful now. More face
more to look at more body.
Molly walked over today
Navy UPS delivery outfit
could be a kinky waitress
at Hooters
still has that thing.
Bright red pin
precarious on top of her
generous left breast,
"I'm here," she announced,
ever the disciple
of her Lee Strasberg past.
"Even though I haven't
seen you in eight years
and why not
I'd still like you to come
to my funeral.
It isn't imminent far as I know.
I've asked Aubyn
to play Sousa marches.
As far as I've gotten."
After this,
she sat down

ready for conversation:
Red bird she saw,
favorite Strindberg play,
neighbor's miniature pony
(she hates miniature ponies).
When she stood up to leave,
45 minutes, decided
in advance, she said,
"Please consider your
funeral answer.
I'd like to know
one way or another.
And tell me what you think
about Chekhov
and green tea."

FRANK

FRANK WAS A HANDSOME older man, one of those men women called Available, although he was a Trump supporter, and many of the local women in his age bracket who had moved upstate after retirement from good work as teachers or nurses or social workers, many of the women, not all but many, were in unions and were Democrats. Still, Frank was a man, and pretty handsome, a man with a twinkle in his eye who could quote a verse or two, had a good pension himself from being an electrician all his life, and he knew, the way some men just do, how to fix whatever was broken. He'd been married to Marie for 43 years, and when she died of lung cancer a few summers ago, he waited and then he declared his availability to Elaine in the post office. Seven months had passed since Marie was buried. Seven long months of Frank on his own. His friend Bill, a widower too, told him to hold off. A year was better. A year was more respectable. But Frank did not want to wait a year. He didn't want to wait at all. He knew Marie would have wanted him to have a companion. She told him so. Bill had been a widower for years now.

One Thursday morning, when he went in to get his mail, almost always predictable, flyers from CVS, from Hannafords, from Walmart—he did not throw them away without looking through them first. Frank did not ever stop looking for bargains. His wife when she was angry—which wasn't all that often, Marie was a placid sort of person—his wife used to call him cheap, but he felt cheap was an unfair way of explaining his reasons for careful. Frank was very careful.

Except in love. He and Marie met through friends. One child. One dog. A son named Eddie. Eddie'd been married and divorced a few times. He and Frank were never close. That's just how it was. Eddie was handsome and pretty silent most of the time. He didn't have any difficulty finding women himself, because he looked strong and appeared to know what he was doing. For many women, that was enough and so Eddie was rarely alone.

Frank put on his good flannel shirt, no rips or tears, only a few years old, the morning he intended to ask Elaine to dinner.

He whistled when he walked over to her, knowing that she who smiled often at him, who was a little younger and eager, he knew that she was a likely *yes*. Not guaranteed, but likely. Frank held himself straight up when he walked into the post office.

And there inside was Elaine. Elaine's in her sixties, a woman who'd already lived a life or two and seemed ready for more. In another era she would have been described as shapely, as round and soft and good. Today when the word gym is often used as a synonym for holy, when taut is considered a positive adjective for bodies, today she might be called a little plump. She looked good. Even eager. Frank was always in a good mood when he knew he'd see Elaine.

Every day out of habit or out of desire, she made up her eyes with black eye liner and used shell pink lipstick, sprayed on perfume. Hers were well thought out country clothes, simple, careful, well-fitting. She wore indigos and other shades of blue, small silver Mexican hoops in her ears.

Her hands were well cared for. Her hands were, she knew, what the postal customers saw. She filed her nails, changed her clear polish twice a week, even polished her thin silver ring. "Hello, Frank," she said when he walked in.

He thought she made "Hello, Frank" sound like the title for a song.

Frank—not as sure of himself as he would like to be, but sure enough—Frank stood a little taller than usual. He forgot about his beer belly and remembered his strong arms.

"Elaine," he said and smiled right at her and then tried to think of something to say besides Nice Day or It Was Supposed to Rain or Have You Tried the Early Corn.

"Almost spring," is what he said. And he wished he could have said something better, wished he was at least right now a little more poetic. Not too much. Just a little. He wished he talked about the daffodils.

She smiled right back and started telling him a story:

"This morning," she said, "Alice Earlham walked in and said, 'I don't understand this President and all the people around him.' Who are they?" Elaine smiled, not even thinking, maybe because she liked him, that one of those people could be Frank. Frank knew his goal was to get her to dinner. He wasn't especially interested in changing her vote. He'd always liked the term Odd Couple. He and Elaine could be an Odd Couple. Some things you didn't have to reveal right away. Marie always claimed she wasn't a political person. He wondered how Elaine would answer that question. She was a Democrat. That's for sure. But how much of a Democrat? And how much of a Republican was he?

"By the way," said Frank, because he didn't want to answer her question—probably rhetorical anyway, and because he couldn't think of a good way to begin. Not that he hadn't considered his options, but none of them seemed quite right. "You're not a vegetarian are you? It's ok with me if you are. But I was wondering. Do you eat meat?"

Elaine smiled at him. "I do," she said. "I really and truly do."

"Do you have a favorite dinner?" Frank felt now he was on safer ground. He did like his meats.

"Prime rib," she said without even a minute's consideration. "Rare if possible, and if not, medium rare. I could eat prime rib every single day and strawberry shortcake with whipped cream for dessert."

"What if that's what we did?" he asked. "Prime rib rare and strawberry shortcake. I know just the place. And you know what else? They make mango margaritas." The fact that he knew about mango margaritas secretly pleased him. "Let's go to REDS tomorrow night. It's right outside of Schenectady. Nice ride on those back roads."

"I could use a nice ride," she said. And smiled right at him.

Before the Country

Our neighbors when we got to Middlefield were different from city neighbors. This was long before Brooklyners discovered the Hudson Valley.

Our New York building, unrenovated city tenement, lobby a cross between a Queens subway stop and a Brazilian whorehouse if you can picture that very same red, is a building full of people who moved in when they were young. The years go quickly, and you don't even notice. No one's so young anymore. It's not a building where people work downtown. None of our neighbors subscribe to the *Wall Street Journal*, or even *The Economist*. It's old style unrenovated New York City, before the whole world knew the name Goldman Sachs, and before everyone named Henry got himself an MBA.

Our next-door neighbor Dolly was a manicurist to the stars when she was young. She's 82 now, and she doesn't leave her studio apartment, even to buy a pint of milk, without ever having perfect nails. Nails are the first thing Dolly sees. She shows me her hands whenever she says hello. Her poodle's Dolly too because she says she doesn't like confusion. She lives right next door to us. She'll knock on the door to say hello, but she always leaves as quickly as she arrives. She says she has things to do.

Roy manages a nearby deli and holds a pastrami party for the whole building for his birthday every year. Everyone eats except we've got one vegetarian—that's probably the best description right there. One out of 24.

People suggested, well intentioned, wanting to give us good advice, that our apartment was not the best place to raise the boys. We don't have space. We live in pollution. What about school? What about play? What about the idyllic childhood that people have in movies and paintings?

Idyllic childhoods are never in the city. No room for a big black Lab in a small city apartment. And as for bicycle paths, although they do exist at last, they exist alongside impossible traffic, right next to taxis and trucks and impatient drivers not wanting to be late.

Maybe that's why we bought our house in Middlefield, for bicycles and neighbors. Not to give up what we have. For more. Even though *more* frightens me, I am drawn to *more*. More books more movies more paintings more experiences. More pairs of shoes. I don't know how many pairs I have. My friend Ken has just three. Even when I was a child, I had more pairs than three. Gold and silver as early as I could choose. When I look down at my feet, I don't like to see the same shoes on my feet every day. I don't like the same bracelets either. My life is endless and changing.

In the country change happens by itself. There is nothing to do but watch. Nothing to do but realize that watching is what our neighbors did when we moved in, the people on our left, a cheerful enough country couple that brought over a cherry pie to say hello, and gave us a tree to plant, a tree to remember them by, a small tree that would grow. "Don't worry. We will help you," is what our neighbor had said. His name is Eddie, and I have never heard anyone call him Edward. I asked him once if Edward was his legal name, and he just laughed. Eddie married Joan, a woman who likes to clean the house and clean the house and clean the house. Eddie likes Joan for cleaning the house. He leaves his shoes outside the back door, even in winter. The floors are always perfect. Joan says she doesn't like to think of feet on her floors. Not just shoes. But she has no choice.

Eddie wears an Ollie North for President T-shirt. He says he has three of them so he can wear them forever. Joan has a bucket for Eddie's boots. He's from a small town near Buffalo, and he met Joan one night at the diner. He said he was eating Salisbury steak.

"What was Joan eating?" I asked him.

"Why do you want to know?"

"For the permanent record."

"OK then," he said. "A big OK. Her favorite is peel and eat all you want shrimps."

"OK then," I said, and so we became friends in a neighborly way. He'd bring over a thermos of coffee and we'd drink it in the yard. He liked his coffee better than mine. He'd say hello to Eli, but in an oddly formal way, almost as though he were saying *Hello Little Man*. His voice was too deep for the boy, and he frightened him. I thought it was because he didn't quite know what to say to children. So many people use a falsetto like they are Little Bo Beep, or they deepen their voice in the opposite direction.

Eddie never said much to them. Not even the general How Are You Doing? And neither did Joan. Eddie was not a personal kind of man. He was not given to any sort of revelation, except for minor preferences: hazelnut coffee at Dunkin Donuts was always his first choice. One morning when he dropped by with his thermos: Hazelnut coffee, his favorite, he said that he and Joan had a child. A boy named Joe, after Joan's older brother. Joe, he said, was in jail for a while. There were no pictures of Joe in the house, they didn't talk about him, they didn't like other people to talk about him either.

"Joe's a good boy," he said. "He's always had a few problems here and there, but who doesn't?" Eddie asked. "Who on earth doesn't have some problems? I'd be the last one on earth," he said, "to pretend I have no problems."

I didn't want to ask what happened. Didn't want not to ask either. "What happened?" I asked after a minute or two. "Tell me what happened."

"I better sit down," he said. "I'll sit right here on this black metal chair. Looks like it could hold me. What's the poundage quotient? Got an idea? Maybe that's the kind of information you don't know."

Eddie wasn't big, but his middle was. He had one of those men stomachs. Hard cannon ball. Joan had Blondie hair. It could have been spray painted onto her head. In a funny way they matched. It's hard to know, but they seemed, from a neighbor's perspective, to actually belong together.

"Joey is 30," he said. "Didn't like school. We tried our best. He got involved with drugs up here. They weren't bad kids. The drugs were bad. We sent him to some programs to straighten him out. Couldn't be done. The police were regulars over here. He got a girl pregnant, a local girl. Nice enough. They had a daughter. Our only grandchild. They called her September like the month. Married. Divorced. He's married again. September went to live with her mother.

You know Joan and I have been married 31 years," Eddie said. He was sitting on a pew bench, a church discard that we had tied onto the top of our car with bungee cords. He sat like a parishioner, rod straight, legs uncrossed. The only difference was his hazelnut coffee.

"Joey lives down in Florida," he said. "Over by Disney World. Not too far. He does odd jobs. His girlfriend—one thing I'll say about Joey, he's never alone very long—his girlfriend is another looker. Where he finds them, I don't know.

You're the neighbor now," said Eddie. "You've been here a while, and I thought you should know. I never said much to the people before you. *Hello* and *goodbye*. Christmas time Joan brought them over some cookies. Funny thing about people. There are some people you might know them forever, forty years or something like that, and you don't want to tell them a thing. Then there are some others you want to sit right down on their church pew and confess."

GREEN

Although I have been trying for a Very Long Time
more or less forever
to Describe What I See to Describe What I Hear
to Describe and Describe
starting with childhood neighbors
Julia C. Steele her secret lover Rebecca McGrath
Ida B. Gordon on the other side
she didn't love her husband Harry
took me years to see what days look like
to look at days especially days in August
when upstate New York Green
far greater than Green
no green words enough for how this feels.
I sit inside lush dense yes miraculous growing life
tomatoes hydrangeas wild orange lilies
even black locust trees
every single year this year especially
because of rain and hope
and because of how life happens in spite of us
and because of us too
although summer does not last forever nothing does
except August and Green
even if you can't describe them not really
you can try you can hint you can even allude
or you can just sit right here.

A Good Meal in Catskill

A Meditation

Breathe In.
Too hot to cook. Maybe we should go out to dinner.

Breathe Out.
Why not?

Breathe In.
Let's try going to the new place in Catskill. Radicci.

Breathe Out.
It's very hot and they probably have no air conditioning.

Breathe In.
Air conditioning doesn't matter. We don't have any either.

Breathe Out.
If it's too hot we can go somewhere else.

Breathe In.
The owner Frank is from Calabria.
He was a barber for 42 years on East 53rd Street.

Breathe Out.
That doesn't mean he can cook.

Breathe In.
We ate there two weeks ago. He cooks the way his mother did.
She was terrific.

Breathe Out.
The meal will be good. And we can ignore any other realities
in a good hot restaurant.

Breathe In.
Just think about good food.

Breathe Out.
After dinner we can walk to the new ice cream store.
It's only two blocks away.

Breathe In.
They have Jane's Ice Cream.

Breathe Out.
The owner makes her own toppings.

Breathe In.
Some people say eating is a meditation.

Breathe Out.
Maybe eating is just eating. Good enough.

What Do I Write Poems About?

(A question people ask all the time,
even when they've read my poems.)

Ken across the street didn't cross
for 25 years, and then, just did.
Ken's daughter, a prison guard,
said yesterday after not talking to us
for ten years or so,
"I wondered how all of you are
in that house."
And then there's Bertha,
policewoman once,
every single day Bertha is Bertha
at the post office—no subject off limits
anymore. One day soon, she'll be
a Big Number, and "Besides,"
she said yesterday,
"It's not like I have a sex life to describe."

LINDA AND OLIVER

The Public Library in the small town
near where we live every summer
has a writing class. I teach it.
Good-looking poetic widow
in her sixties, brightly colored
nurse named Linda
spent last summer on
dating websites.
She dated twelve men. Our whole class
got involved. Even Paul,
the crotchety man,
a good plumber, better story writer
who says he believes
in nothing, says the rest of us
are a "waste of air." We all
got caught up in wanting to know.
The women kept their fingers crossed
for Linda. They all wanted love.
By early September, Linda met Oliver
online. They planned a Friday date.
Oliver, a shop steward,
lived 55 miles away. He writes
poems, picks wildflowers,
and bakes cookies himself
(chocolate chile lime).
Every single one of us
is rooting for Linda and Oliver,
for a life of sex and cookies and poems.

MRS. PARKS

Years ago, our neighbor
in the house across the street,
a prim Protestant baker
of many pies—she had a whole shelf
of Crisco—she, Mrs. Parks, brought
a pie over the week before she died.
She brought her own tea bag too.
Even though we live in the country,
she only wore navy blue suits.
She'd been a nurse at Mt. Sinai
Hospital in New York City
and her three navy blue suits
were from her city time.
"I have a secret," she said.
She ironed she gardened she was busy
busy busy. She did not seem
like a secrets kind of person.
"There was never a Mister Parks,"
she said. "Wait a long time before
you tell anyone that."

Mrs. Parker

Mrs. Parker
regular churchgoer,
competent gardener, maker
of good macaroni and cheese,
she brings some twice a year,
Mrs. Parker called yesterday
she is not a telephone person
to ask if I could come by
for a jar of Dilly Beans.
"No one I know will eat them,"
she said. "Except maybe you."

This Morning, Again

I am here on this porch
maybe there's a word
we've never heard before
deep green blue
and yellow corner
facing up
never less than awe
if I could tell you
what I love so deeply so much
forever how rare to love this way
some of life this long reach of sky
birds and a neighbor saying goodbye
noise and quiet and light
always light even in winter
even late at night and then
every single day in a way
that is worth repeating
we forget get lost
in what we can't do can't change –
when I sit in the very same spot
looking up
just looking up
early every single day
sounds and light and I am here
just right here

Thanksgiving

WE CELEBRATE THANKSGIVING every year in Middlefield, and in a way this meal, days of gathering food and making it, buying the right chestnuts (French, peeled, see-through glass jar), sourdough for stuffing, looking for real non-Ocean Spray cranberries from a cranberry farm, buying Ocean Spray in a can too because everyone, even the foodie types, loves the sweet purplish jelly in a can shaped roll. We prepare for what we all hope is a Big Thanksgiving Welcome for anyone who wants to come; we all give silent thanks that we are able to create and recreate something resembling a new sort of family, where the criteria are desire for community, intention, more than blood, and where eating at our table is the time when all of us are at our best.

Our life is like a religion in a way, a religion with unwritten rules and many unspoken constraints, where abundance and humor are our golden rules. We want to be the family no one ever has. Forgiving. Accepting. Loving. Funny. Open hearted. Maybe like Buddhists without the Buddhism.

We all know how completely impossible this is. How mythical. We know too that all families, blood or not, fall apart and come together, that's just how it is, and that the mythology of how life should be, what it could be, is far greater than what really happens.

I have never trusted anyone who says, all the time, that their life is fine. Or that things are fine. Fine doesn't exist, and yet we persist in our creation of Thanksgiving: in gathering, creating, assembling our own myth.

Although it's true we ourselves fight, in groups of two or three, every year, because by the end of November we are tired, we are all overloaded and overwhelmed, on some silent and secret breakneck path that begins every September and lurches us forward through January when the cold seems to bring life to a halt.

Every single year, forever, Nick says, "Let's change all this, let's not work so hard, we could go out to dinner and anyone can come." But neither of us knows how. Our holiday house policy is this: anyone who wants to come is welcome. There are actually no exceptions. Open arms. A little like an upscale soup kitchen or a Lubavitch home in Crown Heights on Saturday, if you're Lubavitch.

After good friends, a relative or two, there are always contingents of others. Sometimes single people, sometimes couples. People who don't invite other people into their houses, into their apartments. People who keep their lives separate from everyone else. Manuel's cousin Diana comes every single year. Diana, who was beautiful once, one of those women who was actually a choreographer when she was young, who could bend her body in any direction, whose limbs were as beautiful as the most beautiful tree. She's fifty now, and although she could still be beautiful, she isn't. Her windiness has become heavy. She who only eats salads, who says cucumbers are a foul vegetable. Just seeing an unpeeled cucumber makes her nauseous. That's what she says. Peppers, too. She brings rolls made by special needs children as her contribution to our meal. She calls them special-needs rolls. Diana is sad and provocative: one of those people who pushes every single button until you say, (unless you're in a cult or drugged or on some kind of religious voyage) "Stop Diana you are driving me insane." She forces you to say that. She talks about the details of her life without knowing even a little what impact she has on other people.

How sad she seems. And how little room she has for stories that aren't her own. Still she has the kind of physical grace of a woman who once danced all the time, who knew, while she was young, what it meant to glide through air, how to turn her body into a flower.

Neighbors come, people drop in for a drink on their way to somewhere else. The house—more Fellini beautiful than the sort of beauty you'd find in any magazine I can think of: chaos forms its own kind of funny harmony—looks its best when there are people all around. It's a house with many corners, places to hide, places to talk, places to read. Funny old kitchen, a big porcelain sink and right above it, windows facing onto a wide view of mountains, even a horse or two from the neighbor's horse farm. In the middle of the kitchen is one of those old Formica tables that everyone's relatives had. The table makes me think of soup. It's light grey, with a top that's easy to wipe clean. It doesn't belong in the kitchen really. Different era. Different mood. We should have a Long French country table: beautiful wood, surrounded by chairs. Instead it's got a rag tag Aunt Sadie flea market quality that is more or less in keeping with the rest of our house. Dishes are stacked on an old French pie rack, a high vertical V. The kitchen leads right into the dining room, a big enough room painted that green color that is in country houses and nowhere else. Dutch yellow's the name of the trim.

Down the middle of the room is one of those everybody-can-fit-if-they-breathe-in tables. We bought it our first month in the house, and found a man who could make us leaves. The room is big, and when the leaves are in, the table goes from wall to wall.

If we turn it into a Last Supper Replica, with a second table at right angles, we can fit in a few more. But maybe because of the Last Supper, that's not something we tend to do.

What I Want To Tell You (Is This Is This Is This)

Some places, not big history cities
Rome Athens Delhi Nairobi Machu Picchu
or places requiring tourist offices and maps—
some places, mostly obscure villages, small
as easy to recognize as love.
My childhood—ordinary house
painted brown. A few maple trees. For years
I didn't see full fragrant anywhere else
for years I saw logic
what passes for order
what real life was supposed to be
then I went by myself
to a small village in Greece
white-washed monastery.
I walked up a dirt path cypress trees
into a room so beautiful
I knew I'd never seen beauty before
strong deep scent, what was it
I still don't know
exactly the way you feel
when someone touches you
and you know you've never
been touched before what you want
is to be touched like that again and again.
This place, imperfect village, some people
don't like each other don't have enough money
too many kids, cult came so did a flood
trees fall economy difficult
still I am not romanticizing when I
tell you I want to tell you this,
I want you to know

so you'll maybe be able to recognize
some places unimaginable beauty
not pretty flowers in a glass jar
good beauty nothing fleeting
nothing occasional
this place is where
what you suspected all along can happen.
Bright red dreams.

IMPOSSIBLE TO DESCRIBE

to tell you what beauty is what beauty looks like
how it feels sitting on this porch
a porch I've tried thousands of times to explain
to bring you here to explain what it feels like
to sit where I always sit every single day
even on those days that aren't nearly as beautiful
as this one
today here I am in my now springless
Freudian chaise covered in blankets and pillows
in the perfect corner of life
facing trees and a field and a sky that is the same
as sky astounding all day no matter what happens
in this world and there are birds and birds and light.

What This Place Looks Like

Middlefield
one of those villages
doesn't much change
same kinds of problems
what life looks like
how life is
lived usually

real families,
messy, earning
some kind of living
or trying to.
Food each week
potatoes in ten-pound
bags onions too
all in the basement
if there is a basement.
Supermarket bread.

Weekender New Yorkers
carry bread in their cars.
They say
there's no bread
in upstate New York.
Coffee either.
Though locals
drink plenty of coffee.

Some tell us each choice
is a moral decision.

All our houses continue
breathing.

Zucchini and tomatoes
every summer
if we are lucky.
How we use them
depends on books
we read.
On the books
we don't.
On grandmothers.
And what we remember.
We all try for pleasantries.
Hot. Cold.
Rain is expected.
I heard a storm
will come.
Not enough rain.
Maybe tomorrow
we can say more.

ACKNOWLEDGMENTS

This book actually started in the canned vegetables aisle of Slater's supermarket in Cairo, New York. Not long after we moved in, I asked Bud Slater if I could teach a writing class there. The requirement was that people had to shop at Slater's. He announced the class the same way he announced supermarket sales. He generously provided black and white notebooks and pens, and snacks from Slater's after class. We all wrote about our lives.

Slater's was sold to Great American, then Hannafords. And our class moved to the Cairo Public Library.

Cairo Public Library, a miracle of a place in the midst of a poor county, a library with computers, a great children's book room, rental movies, contemporary fiction and a rich collection, has been run for many years by Debra Kamecke, a patient book-loving idealist, a writer herself.

Lucy and Robin persisted there too.

Thank you to Bonnie Sue Marcus and Poets and Writers for all those years.

So many people contributed stories of their own, and stories of people they know. I'm grateful to have heard them all, and to have had the chance to write them down.

Thank you to Bruce, Cliff, Steve, Noah, Chesray, Abigail, Andrew, Patch, Terry, Lory, Alarik, Mitch, Shelley, Elizabeth, Thomas, Ines, Dave, Kim, Alex, Aurora, Angela, Lucinda, and everyone else who made life amazing.

Thank you to Cairo Writers Tony, Dorian, Lucille, Bill, Reba, Margaret, Michelle, Carol, Shelly, Michael and Jean.

Thank you to Lauren Grosskopf for patience and beauty.

Thank you to Matthew Septimus for unbelievable photographs.

Thank you to my invaluable sisters writing group: Breena and Cheryl Clarke.

Thank you to Edite Kroll who understands.

Thank you thank you to Ruth Thompson poet friend, editor, publisher, and good friend to so many writers. Thank you to Don Mitchell for your skill.

Thank you thank you thank you to Peter Odabashian. Without Whom.

Thanks to the editors:

WNYC/Morning Edition: "Of Neighbors Who Fall in Love with Each Other"

New York Society Library: "How We Found Our Real Estate Lawyer"

NOW Journal, HFWW: "Mrs. Parks," "Arlette's Husband," "Tom and Jane"

Alimentum: "Made in Russia," "On the Verge"

Jewish Currents: "What Happened to Phil," "Middlefield"

Na'amat Women: "Puzzles"

ABOUT ESTHER COHEN

Esther Cohen is a writer, teacher, bookdoctor, and labor activist. For many years she ran Bread and Roses, a national cultural program for workers. She started a program called Unseen America and co-founded the Clara Lemlich Awards for women activists.

Her poem/photograph series with Matthew Septimus is featured at On Being. She is the author of six books, including *Breakfast With Allen Ginsberg* (poetry), *Bookdoctor* (fiction) and *Don't Mind Me and Other Jewish Lies,* illustrated by Roz Chast.

Milton Keynes UK
Ingram Content Group UK Ltd.
UKHW010249221123
432980UK00005B/458